The Penguin Music Scores

EDITED BY GORDON JACOB

J. S. BACH

Brandenburg Concertos No. 1 in F and No. 2 in F

WITH A BIOGRAPHICAL NOTE BY FRANK HOWES AND
AN INTRODUCTION BY GORDON JACOB

PENGUIN BOOKS

PENGUIN BOOKS

Published by the Penguin Group
27 Wrights Lane, London W8 5TZ, England
Viking Penguin Inc., 40 West 23rd Street, New York, New York 10010, USA
Penguin Books Australia Ltd, Ringwood, Victoria, Australia
Penguin Books Canada Ltd, 2801 John Street, Markham, Ontario, Canada L3R 1B4
Penguin Books (NZ) Ltd, 182–190 Wairau Road, Auckland 10, New Zealand

Penguin Books Ltd, Registered Offices: Harmondsworth, Middlesex, England

Published in Penguin Books 1950

3 5 7 9 10 8 6 4 2

Made and printed in Great Britain by
Richard Clays Ltd (The Chaucer Press), Bungay, Suffolk

JOHN SEBASTIAN BACH

(1685–1750)

BACH's biography is a plain tale, in four main chapters, of a working musician's career in provincial Germany during the first half of the eighteenth century. The fact that he happened to be a genius, though it means much to us, did not carry great weight with his contemporaries, to whom he was chiefly known as an expert on organs and in his later years as a remarkable contrapuntist. A few happy episodes, which constitute the best-known anecdotes about him, show that genius will out, however. Of these his reception by Frederick the Great at Potsdam in 1747 is the most picturesque and the most significant. There, at any rate, one great man recognised the greatness of another. Bach, however, never suffered the misfortunes that overtook Handel, nor knew the slow misery which crushed Mozart. His career, if humdrum, was at any rate secure, and he was able to bring up a family in reasonable comfort and to launch at least three musicians successfully upon the world.

He was himself the product of a long line of musicians, and is the greatest of a clan whose history is known over a period of 200 years. He traced his ancestry back to one, Veit Bach, a miller and baker who left Hungary in the sixteenth century to settle in Thuringia, where he could practise the Lutheran religion without molestation. Veit Bach died in 1619, and his son, nicknamed Hans the Minstrel, was the first professional of a long line of musicians that became extinct only in 1845, when the last of Sebastian's male heirs died.

Johann Sebastian, the greatest of this family of organists, Cantors, *Kapellmeisters* (= Director of Music), town waits and instrumentalists, was born on 21 March, 1685, an *annus mirabilis* in musical history, in which not only Bach but Handel and Domenico Scarlatti came into the world they were so amply and variously to enrich. Sebastian was the youngest son of Johann Ambrosius Bach, court and town musician at Eisenach, a small town in Central Germany – Thuringia lies due north of

Bavaria and east of Saxony', and contains Weimar as its chief city. Of Sebastian's early years all that is known is that he learned music, including the violin, from his father, that he went to school at the age of 8, and was bereaved first of his mother and then in less than a year of his father before he was 10. He was then taken into the home of his eldest brother, Johann Christoph, who was living in the neighbouring town of Ohrdruf, where Sebastian went to school from 1695 to 1700. He did well at school, and when it became difficult to remain 'ob deficium hospitiorum' (which may mean accommodation at home rather than inability to pay the fees), a place was found for him by one of his masters in the musical establishment of St Michael's Church at Lüneburg, far away to the north. Here his stay of three years committed him to the career of a church musician, and his visits to Hamburg and Celle during his residence in north Germany were influential on his development. At Hamburg he heard the great organist Adam Reinken, and at Celle, where the court was conducted after the manner of a minor Versailles, he became acquainted with the French style, as represented, for instance, by Couperin.

Two stories are told of his boyhood, which ended when he returned to Thuringia in 1703 at the age of 18 to take up his first job in the ducal orchestra at Weimar. The first is of his precocity as a little boy of not more than 11, when, having exhausted his brother's teaching, he surreptitiously removed a roll of his brother's manuscript from a bookcase and copied out its contents – pieces by the chief composers of the time – at night. When he had completed his task, which took six months of moonlight nights, he was discovered and his book confiscated. The other is of one of his journeys from Hamburg back to Lüneburg. His money was gone when he came to an inn from which savoury smells proceeded and sharpened his already keen appetite. Suddenly a window was opened and a couple of herrings' heads thrown out. The hungry lad seized them and had hardly torn them open when he discovered a Danish ducat in each, which enabled him to have his meal and still leave him some change. He never discovered his benefactor or why the episode occurred, but he used to tell the tale in later life with relish.

The post at Weimar was temporary, and after a

few months he moved to Arnstadt to become organist at the New Church. This was the opening of the second chapter of his life's story, which is that of his five official appointments: Arnstadt (1703–7), Mülhausen (1707–8), Weimar (1708–17), Cöthen (1717–23), and Leipzig (1723–50). These employments have a direct bearing on his output as a composer, for up to and beyond his time the modern sharp distinction between performer and composer was not drawn. Bach was an executant musician who wrote music for immediate use. He needed music for performance, so he added some of his own to what he could find of other people's. As a composer, therefore, he is the supreme craftsman turning out work needed for specific purposes in the job he was holding at the time. There are only a few exceptions in his output of music not written *ad hoc*: the forty-eight Preludes and Fugues were composed to demonstrate a thesis; the *B Minor Mass* had a curious inspiration in personal ambition; *The Musical Offering* was instigated by Frederick the Great; and *The Art of Fugue* was a theoretical work of music for music's sake that grew out of *The Musical Offering*.

His first three appointments may be taken together as the chapter of biography that sees him established as a church musician. At Arnstadt his work was that of organist but not that of choirmaster, and owing to his dissatisfaction with the way things were run there he refused with surprising stubbornness to take any responsibility for the singing in the church. He went to Arnstadt with the intention of making himself a good organist, and with this end in view he sought leave of absence to go to Lübeck to hear and study the work of the great Buxtehude. He put in a deputy and went off for a month. But he overstayed his leave, so that he was away for four months. The consistory naturally objected, and complained further that his accompaniments to the hymns had become too florid, and asked in addition by what right he had allowed a 'strange maiden' into the organ loft and let her make music. The strange maiden was his cousin, Maria Barbara Bach, who became his first wife a year later and subsequently the mother of Carl Philipp Emanuel. There is a story of a rumpus with the undisciplined boys of the choir in the public square at Arnstadt, which, if it does not explain Bach's dissatisfaction with the job, at any rate confirms the unsatisfactory state of affairs in the choir. So, after four years in his first post, he took another organ at St Blasius at Mülhausen, where, however, he stayed an even shorter time. The trouble here was theological. His personal relations with the church authorities were more cordial, but religious controversy was detrimental to church music, to which by a reversal of his attitude at Arnstadt he now attached more importance, and so when he was again offered a place in the ducal establishment at Weimar he accepted it. His short stay of less than a year (1707–8) was noteworthy for his marriage and his first publication, the cantata *God is my King* composed for the annual civic service. At Arnstadt he had written his first church cantata (for Easter) and some organ music.

At Weimar, where he remained for nine years, his work continued on the same lines. Much of his greatest organ music was written now, and some of his church cantatas. His fame as an organist was established, and he became known as an expert to be consulted about old or new organs. His official position was that of court organist, and in 1714 he was promoted to the status of *Konzertmeister*, but to the coveted position of *Kapellmeister* he was not ad-

vanced when the vacancy occurred. Disappointment in this matter, and the difficulty of a divided loyalty to the two dukes, who by a curious constitutional arrangement shared the executive office of the dukedom, ultimately led him to accept an offer from the neighbouring court of Cöthen. But his time at Weimar was not unhappy, for he had a good salary that was constantly being raised and plenty of congenial society, including that of the younger duke. Some echo of the amenity of life in these ducal courts reaches us in the strains of the familiar *Sheep may safely graze*, which comes from the cantata *Was mir behagt*, composed for the birthday of the neighbouring Duke of Weissenfels and directed by Bach there after a banquet in the great hall.

A picturesque episode that was told in Bach's obituary notice and was repeated by Forkel in his biography belongs to Bach's Weimar period. This was the projected competition between him and Louis Marchand, the French organist of Versailles, who was at that time (1717) touring Europe as a virtuoso of international repute. The prompter and promoter of the contest was the *Konzertmeister* at Dresden – there is no modern equivalent of that official title of the second in command of a musical establishment; Leader of the Orchestra is its modern meaning. This man, Jean Baptiste Volumier, though himself a Frenchman, seems to have wished to take down the pride of his fellow-countryman and knew that Sebastian Bach was the man to do it. He therefore invited Bach over to Dresden and secreted him where he could hear Marchand play; he then persuaded Bach to issue a courteous challenge in which the challenger undertook to execute extemporaneously any musical feat required of him, if his antagonist would do the same. The challenge was accepted, and the contest prepared with the connivance of the king. But when the prescribed hour arrived Marchand did not appear – he had left Dresden early that morning by special coach.

There was some difficulty about moving from Weimar to Cöthen, as the duke at first refused to release him and even put him under arrest for a month. His new employer, however, Prince Leopold of Anhalt-Cöthen, was personally friendly, and he enjoyed the position of *Kapellmeister*. Against this was to be set the fact that the court was Calvinistic – and there is evidence that Bach the Lutheran did not like Cal-

vinism – which meant that Bach did not play the small organ in the chapel and in fact gave up all connection with church music during the six years he remained at Cöthen. This break in his career, however, was no loss for posterity, since we owe to it most of the chamber and orchestral music. He was at the head of an establishment of seventeen players, and for them he wrote the sonatas, concertos, and orchestral suites in order to enlarge the small repertory he found when he took up his duties. In addition he made two major and two minor compilations during his time at Cöthen. In 1721 he sent off to the Margrave of Brandenburg the six concertos for various combinations of instruments which has immortalised that potentate's name, and in 1722 he published the first set of preludes and fugues known as *The Well-Tempered Clavier*.* In 1720 he began a collection of small teaching pieces for his own son Wilhelm Friedmann, and in 1722 Anna Magdalena's Little Book, which contained what came subsequently to be known as the French suites. This

* 'Clavier' is the generic name in German for the keyboard, and is applicable, therefore, to clavichord, harpsichord, and pianoforte; not, however, to the organ.

Anna Magdalena was his second wife, whom he married in 1721. His first wife had died during his absence at Carlsbad with his prince in the summer of 1720, and it is said that Bach knew nothing of it until he returned to find her dead and buried. By her he had seven children in their thirteen years of married life, of whom Wilhelm Friedmann and Carl Philipp Emanuel and a daughter survived him. Both sons inherited a good deal of their father's talent, and from the second family Johann Christian made a great reputation for himself as the 'London Bach', who gave concerts, composed in the new *galant* style, and had considerable influence on the development of young Mozart.

The Brandenburg Concertos, which are an epit-one of Bach's instrumental genius and stand at the cross-roads in musical history where chamber and orchestral music parted, and where the unitary *ritor-nello* form reached its highest development before its supersession by sonata-form, were commissioned by the Elector of Brandenburg, possibly at Karlsbad in 1718, possibly at Cöthen when he was on a visit to Bach's master. The recipient does not appear to have appreciated their value in spite of this courtly

address, for at his death the manuscript scores, which showed no sign of having been used, were sold as a job lot. The *Well-Tempered Clavier* was composed and compiled as a demonstration of the desirability of the system of tuning keyboard instruments known as equal temperament, by which the errors of in-tonation due to anomalies in Nature's own harmonic series are so distributed as to make all twelve major and minor keys available without gross offence to the ear. Twenty-two years later he added a second volume. The complete work is therefore affection-ately known as *The 48*.

About the time of Bach's second marriage his em-ployer also took to himself a wife. This change at court was the first cause of his removing to Leipzig. The death of Johann Kuhnau (the composer of the Biblical Sonatas for keyboard), which caused a vacancy in the school and church of St Thomas, was the occasion. A secondary motive was concern for his children's education in Lutheran schools and sub-sequently at the University. Bach mentions this in a letter to a friend. There was some competition for this important post. Bach submitted a cantata in February 1723 as the usual proof of his skill, but he also performed his new *St John Passion* in March; in May he was given the appointment, in which he remained for the rest of his life. All the great choral works come from this period: the *St Matthew Passion* followed the *St John* in 1729, the lost *St Mark Passion* was composed for 1731; the *B Minor Mass*, whose composition was piecemeal and peculiar, was begun in 1733; the *Christmas Oratorio*, consisting of six cantatas in sequence, was first performed in 1734; and the huge collection of church cantatas designed to cover the ecclesiastical year with five distinct cycles, was amassed during his first twenty years there. He wrote secular cantatas for various occasions, and took up composition for the organ again. In 1729 he was appointed conductor of the Telemann Musical Society of the University, for which he composed and adapted instrumental concertos which he played with his sons and pupils.

Musically, therefore, posterity has no cause to regret his removal from Cöthen and his return to church music, but his personal life was marred by petty vexations without number for about fifteen years. He had a dispute with the University about certain duties at St Paul's church; he had the usual

dispute about the choice of hymns with one of the clergy of St Nicholas's; he had a final row with his immediate superior, the headmaster (Rector) of St Thomas's school, which supplied the choristers for the various churches in Leipzig. This dismal and rather sordid quarrel, which arose out of a question of discipline and the appointment of school prefects, dragged on for two years, and was composed only after Bach had appealed to the King of Saxony and had had his ruffled pride smoothed when the king, to whom he had dedicated the *B Minor Mass*, came to Leipzig at Easter in 1738. These affronts to his dignity brought out all the native obstinacy of his character, and were met with the quick temper which was also one of his traits. But through these troubled years he had a happy home life: his sons were growing up and as they went out into the world they did well, with the exception of Gottfried Bernhard, who got into debt and absconded from his organistship. His daughter Elisabeth married one of his pupils, Johann Christoph Altnikol. Glimpses of his home life can be obtained from the letters he exchanged with a cousin who had lived with him for a time in his student days, letters that mention gifts of wine and carnation plants and a request for a linnet that could sing for Anna Magdalena. During the last years of his life he had increasing trouble with his eyes, but he went on preparing manuscripts for publication.

A family event of 1747 led to the most picturesque incident in his whole career. For Philipp Emanuel's wedding Sebastian visited Berlin, accompanied by another son, Friedmann. Frederick the Great, a keen amateur flautist, had expressed to Philipp, who was in his employment, a desire to meet his great father. Frederick insisted on Sebastian's immediate attendance upon his arrival at Potsdam, and took him on a tour of the palace, showing him its organs and his new Silbermann pianofortes, which Bach thought an improvement on the earlier models which he had adversely criticised. He improvised on them fugues on a subject given him by the king. The royal theme was further developed on Bach's return home, and from it came *The Musical Offering*, which he sent to the king. Fired by this challenge to his contrapuntal skill he embarked on the *Art of Fugue*, but his health broke in 1749. He had an operation on his eyes by an English oculist, John Taylor, who re-

ported in his autobiography that he found the effects of paralysis which made a cure impossible. Through a spring made depressing for him by his medical treatment Bach continued to prepare for the engraver another set of eighteen chorale preludes, and wrote fifteen of them with his own hand. In July he faltered and asked for his daughter Lizzy, who came with her husband, to whom Bach dictated two more and the opening of a prelude on the chorale *When we stand in deepest need*. If Bach had any premonition of death he certainly did not think of it as the hour of need, so he bade his son-in-law write at the head of it the title of another hymn sung to the same tune, 'Before thy throne, O God, I stand'. The music breaks off abruptly in the middle of a bar — Bach had composed his last note. On 18 July, 1750, he had a remarkable rally and could see again for a while, but a stroke quickly supervened and after ten days of fever he breathed his last on the evening of 28 July and was buried on the last day of the month.

THESE two concertos differ from No. 3, which has already been issued in this series, in possessing *concertante* groups of solo instruments which are used in alternation with the main group or *tutti*.

CONCERTO NO. I

In this concerto an unusually large and powerful *concertante* group is used. It consists of three oboes, two horns, bassoon, and 'violino piccolo'. This last instrument was, as its name shows, a small-sized violin. In the original score its part is written a minor third lower than the rest of the string parts, with the key signature of D major. It can be deduced from this that its strings were tuned a minor third higher than those of the standard violin, the transposition enabling normal fingering to be employed so that the part could be played without trouble by a player accustomed to the normal-sized instrument. The use of this instrument was discontinued when violin technique had improved sufficiently for very high notes to be obtainable on the ordinary violin. In

Grove's *Dictionary of Music and Musicians* a remark of Leopold Mozart's is quoted, showing that by 1756 the violino piccolo had become unnecessary and was already practically obsolete in the orchestra. It continued, however, to be used by dancing masters, and was, when so employed, called a 'kit' in this country.

The horn parts were written for horns in F and were transposed a fifth higher than the actual sounds. They are printed here at the sounded pitch.

The continuo part consists of the bass of the structure which was filled in on the harpsichord. The continuo player controlled and kept together the performance from his place at the keyboard, occasionally beating time when things threatened to become unsteady. Conducting by means of a baton did not begin until a century or so had elapsed after the completion of the Brandenburg concertos in 1721.

In this particular concerto the *concertante* group is sufficiently strong and sonorous to balance the *tutti*, and consequently there is more actual combination of the two groups and less use of them in alternation than in works where the *concertante* group is too weak to compete on anything like equal terms with the *tutti*. This must have been even truer in the early eighteenth century when there were several oboe players to each part instead of only one, as is the case to-day.

With regard to the writing for horns, the agility expected of the players and the great altitude of much of their parts is in strong contrast to the relatively static nature and lower pitch of the horn parts of later composers of the classical period.

The horns used by Bach were, like those of the classical period, valveless, and could only produce notes of the harmonic series from their fundamental note. In order to get scale-passages it was necessary to use the upper partials from the eighth harmonic upwards, and therefore such passages could be played only in the higher registers of the instrument. It will be observed that from the note F (first space) upwards stepwise movement is freely used. Below this only notes of the common chord of F were possible.

It will also be noticed that the rapid passage-work which Bach gives to the horns is mainly stepwise in its motion. The notes were obtained entirely by varying lip pressure (*embouchure*), and stepwise movement from the adjacent upper partials would obviously be easier and more secure than rapid skips. Horn and trumpet players in Bach's time cultivated these high notes, but with the change in style which came in with the swing-over to harmonic rather than solely contrapuntal writing, and which resulted in the horns being used very largely as cohesive elements in the texture rather than as active melodic instruments, players ceased to practise the art of executing rapid passages high up in their compass. With the introduction of valves it became possible to write scalically at any pitch within the horn's compass, and this made it unnecessary to subject the players to the strain of producing so many high notes. Thus it is that present-day horn players find parts such as Bach writes in this concerto exceedingly difficult and fatiguing, and they must be forgiven if there is an occasional 'fluffy' note. Horns fitted with 'Bflatalto' crooks are best employed here. They bring the parts within easily negotiated upward limits of pitch.

With regard to Bach's orchestration in general we may say that, though he understood perfectly the capabilities of the instruments and players of his day, the polyphonic idiom in which he wrote did not give very much scope for differentiation between the char-

Bach:
Brandenburg
Concertos
No. 1 in F
and No. 2
in F

acters of the instruments. Each one had to play a part in the general melodic movement out of which the texture was woven, and any harmonic support that might be felt necessary was supplied by the continuo.

The form of the first and third movements is that generally associated with Bach. There is a main theme which recurs from time to time either in whole or in part and in various keys related to the key of the movement. These appearances are separated by episodes derived from or akin to the main theme, and the rhythmic movement set up at the beginning is maintained unbroken throughout. Thus a high degree of unity and continuity is achieved. In this concerto the main part of the last movement is followed by a delightful little dance suite consisting of a Minuet and Polacca and two Trios which are so organised as to form what really amounts to a continuous fourth movement, and are designed to show off the paces of various groups of instruments in turn.

The middle movement, an Adagio in D minor, is a very beautiful example of the kind of slow movement into which Bach put his deepest feeling and emotion, and which defies formal analysis. The melodic interes. is divided between the first oboe and the violino piccolo. The bass instruments also take part in it occasionally. The rest of the orchestra supply accompanying parts; the expressive little figure of three notes which first appears in the ninth bar on the oboes, echoed by the strings, plays an important part in the movement, and its poignancy is much increased by the 'false relation' in the bass. The horns are silent in this movement.

CONCERTO NO. 2

Here the *concertante* instruments are flute, oboe, trumpet, and violin, the compass of all of which lies in the bright 'soprano' register. The *tutti* consists of strings and continuo.

The music of the first and third movements is charged with the utmost brilliance and gaiety, to which the very high-pitched trumpet part makes a substantial contribution.

Bach writes for trumpet in F, and in the original score its part is written in the key of C, a fourth below the actual sounds. We print it here at the sounded pitch, which shows clearly to the eye its dizzy altitude. The part in fact often looks more like a flute than a

15

trumpet part. Its execution is a problem to-day, and though a skilled player can, with a good deal of strain and anxiety, manage most of it on the ordinary trumpet in B flat, the very high passages are safer when played an octave lower. Some players possess a 'piccolo trumpet' in F on which the part can be played exactly as Bach wrote it.

The reason for the extreme height of most of the scalic passages is the same as that given for the horn parts in the First Concerto.

The flute part also is much more effective in the ensemble than was usual at that period. Bach makes liberal use of its brilliant upper register instead of chiefly confining it to its weaker middle notes, which would have been more in accordance with the practice of the day and indeed with his own usual procedure.

The writing for all the solo instruments is on a very high plane of virtuosity, and the effect of a fine spirited performance is extraordinarily invigorating.

The form of the first and third movements is the usual Bach form noted before, except that in the third movement the construction is more decidedly fugal than the first, and the four *concertante* instruments are thrown into stronger relief than ever in this movement by the transparency of the accompanying *tutti* parts.

This concerto in fact contrasts strongly with the First in this respect. In the First the *concertante* group is to a large extent actually combined with the *tutti* to form a definitely orchestral effect. In the Second the *concertante* parts are far more exposed and are more 'solo' in character.

The middle movement, an Andante in D minor, is conceived as a Trio for flute, oboe, and violin, accompanied only by the violoncellos and continuo. It is reflective in mood and is of great beauty. The ever-moving bass, though it is not a true ground bass, almost has the effect of one, and binds together the texture formed by the quasi-canonical writing for the three soloists above it. The trumpet is silent during this movement. Its entry at the beginning of the last movement is all the more electrifying for this.

GORDON JACOB

Brandenburg Concerto No. 1

I

JOHANN SEBASTIAN BACH

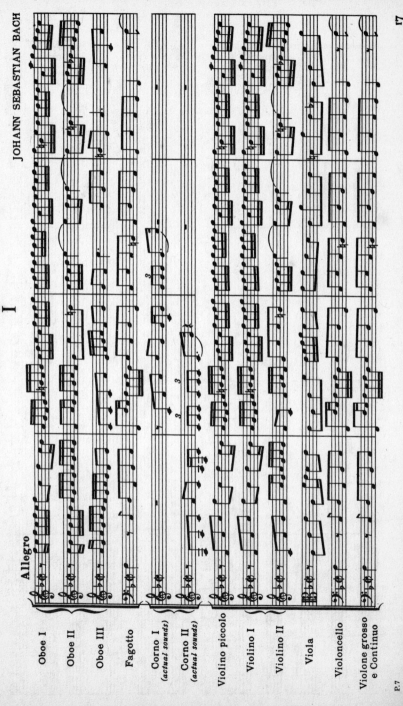

Allegro

Oboe I
Oboe II
Oboe III
Fagotto
Corno I *(actual sounds)*
Corno II *(actual sounds)*
Violino piccolo
Violino I
Violino II
Viola
Violoncello
Violone grosso e Continuo

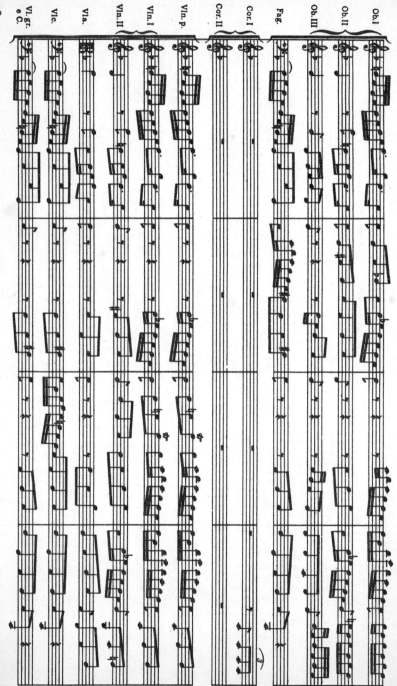

10
Ob. I
Ob. II
Ob. III
Fag.
Cor. I
Cor. II
Vln. p.
Vln. I
Vln. II
Vla.
Vlc.
Vl. gr. e C.
10

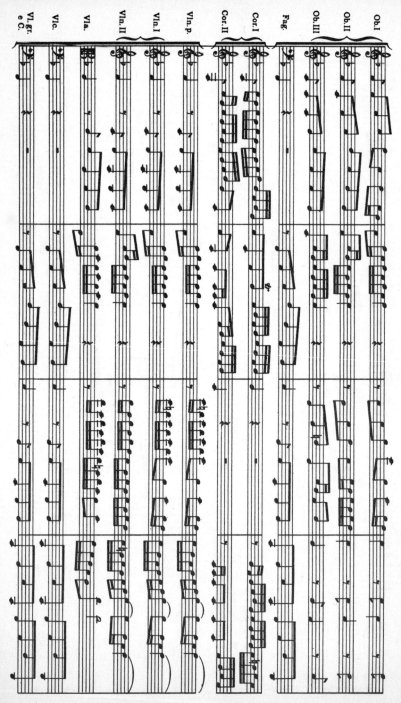

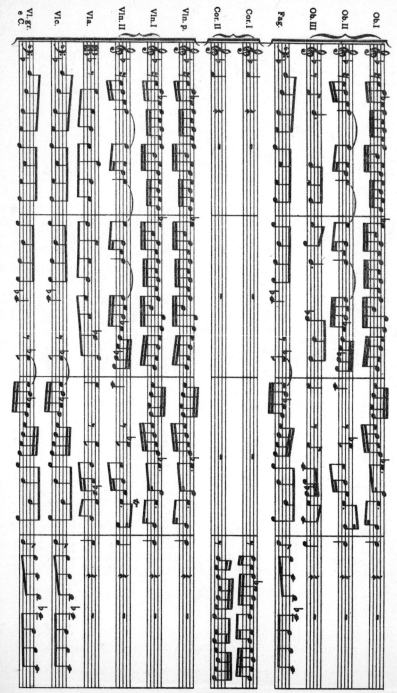

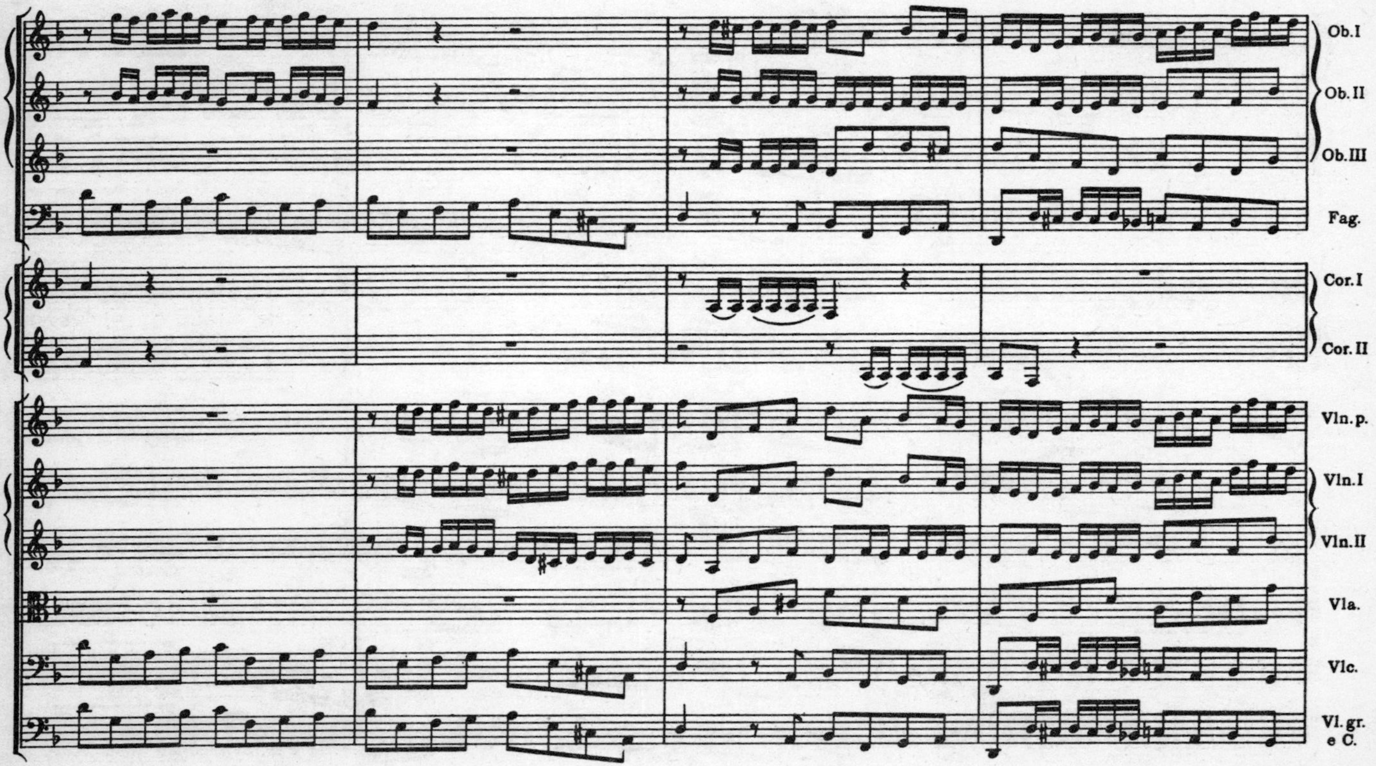
Ob. I
Ob. II
Ob. III
Fag.
Cor. I
Cor. II
Vln. p.
Vln. I
Vln. II
Vla.
Vlc.
Vl. gr. e C.

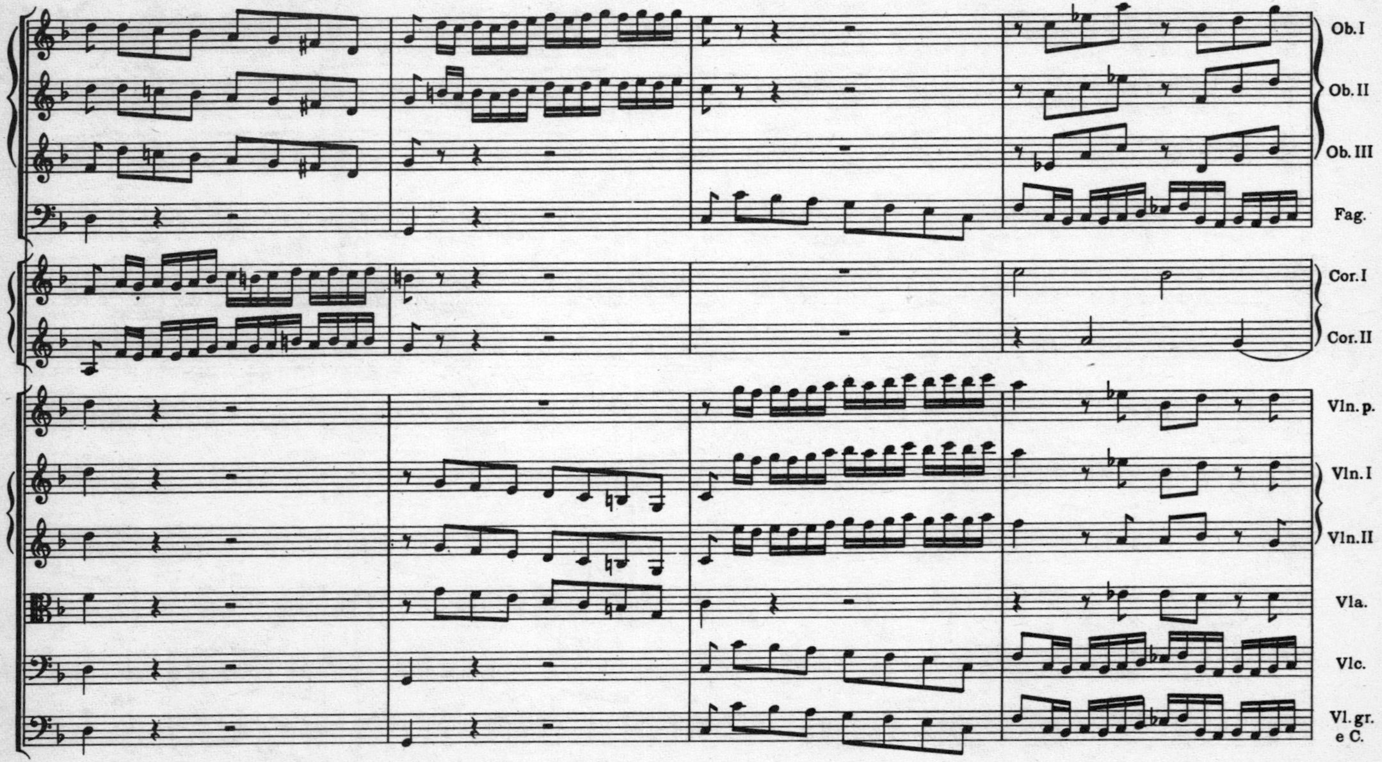
Ob. I
Ob. II
Ob. III
Fag.
Cor. I
Cor. II
Vln. p.
Vln. I
Vln. II
Vla.
Vlc.
Vl. gr. e C.

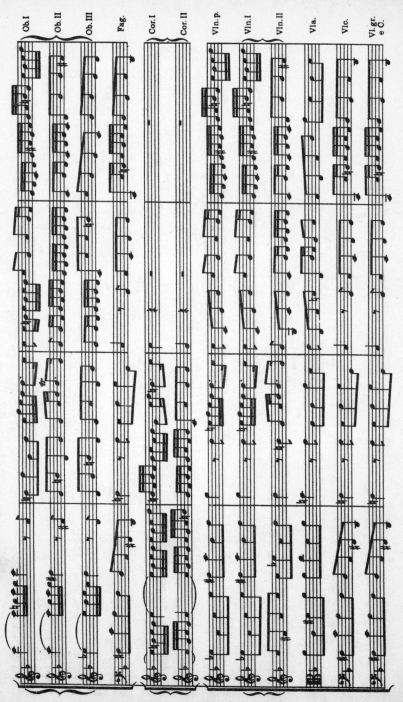

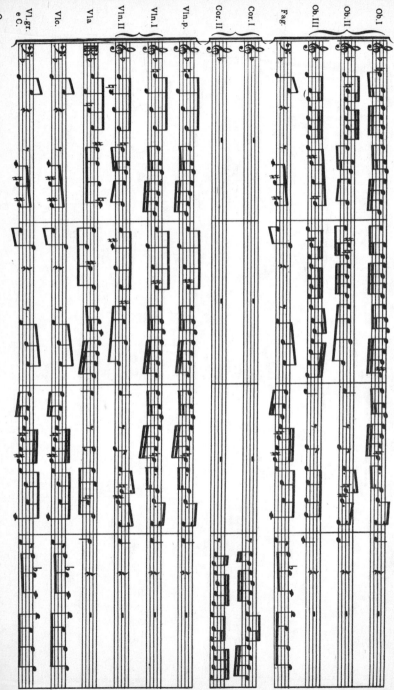

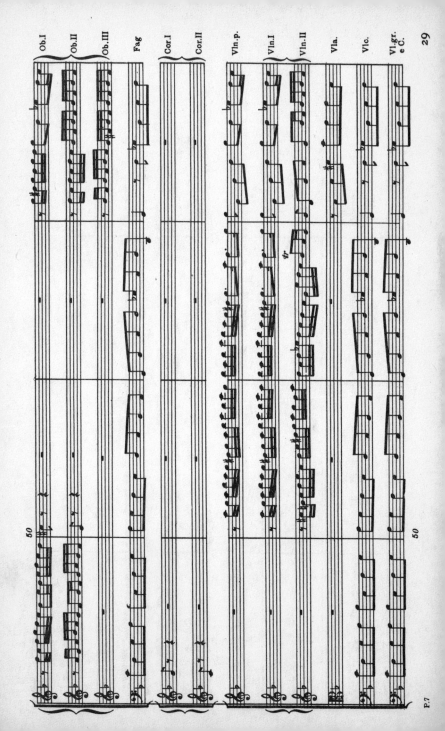

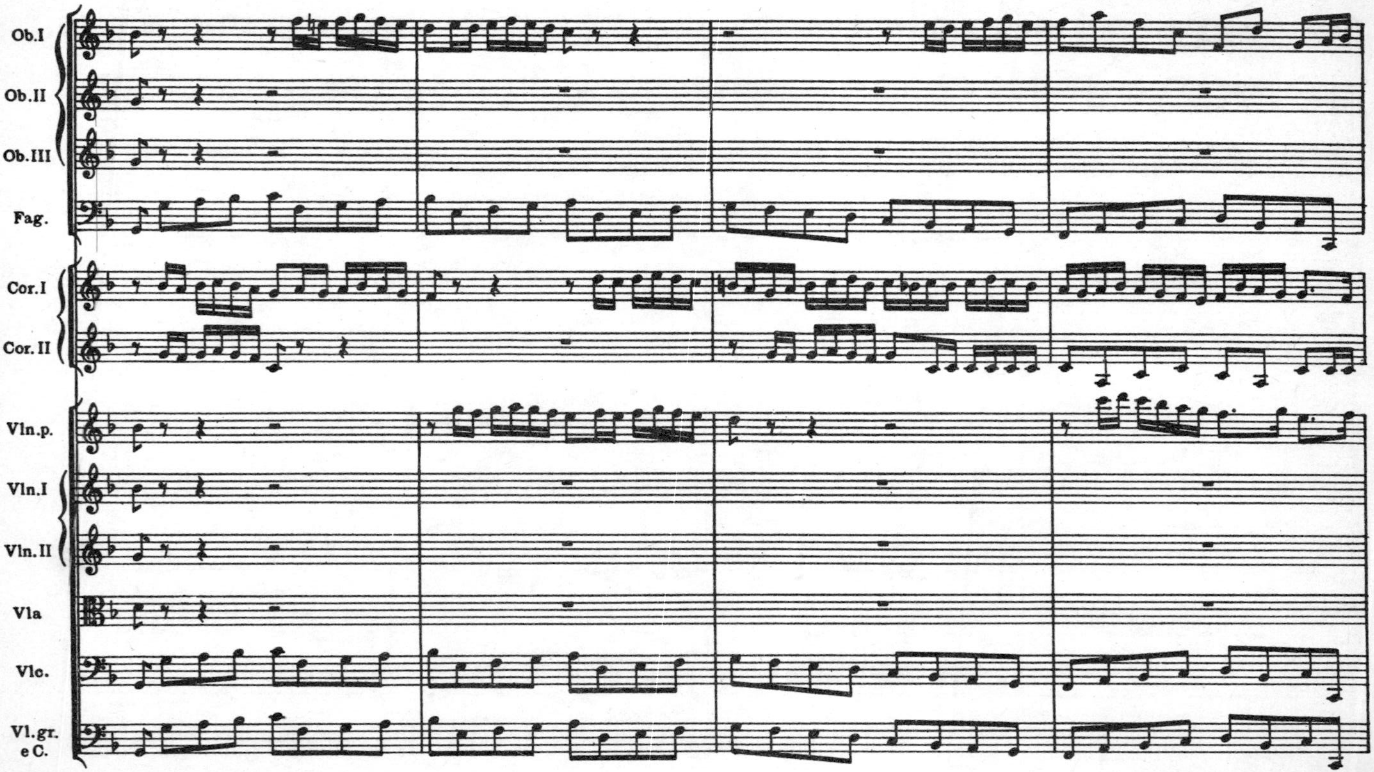
Ob.I
Ob.II
Ob.III
Fag.
Cor.I
Cor.II
Vln.p.
Vln.I
Vln.II
Vla
Vlc.
Vl.gr.
e C.

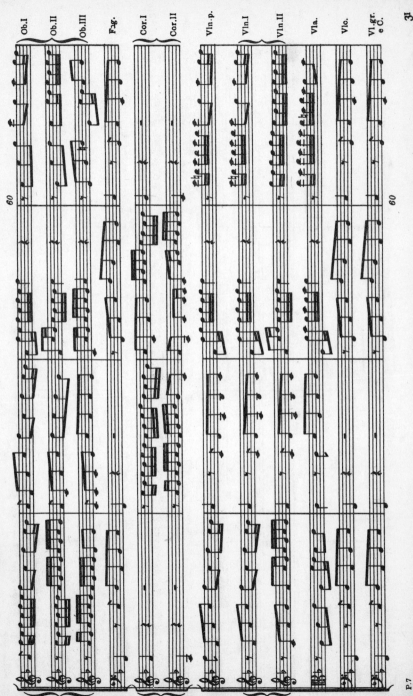

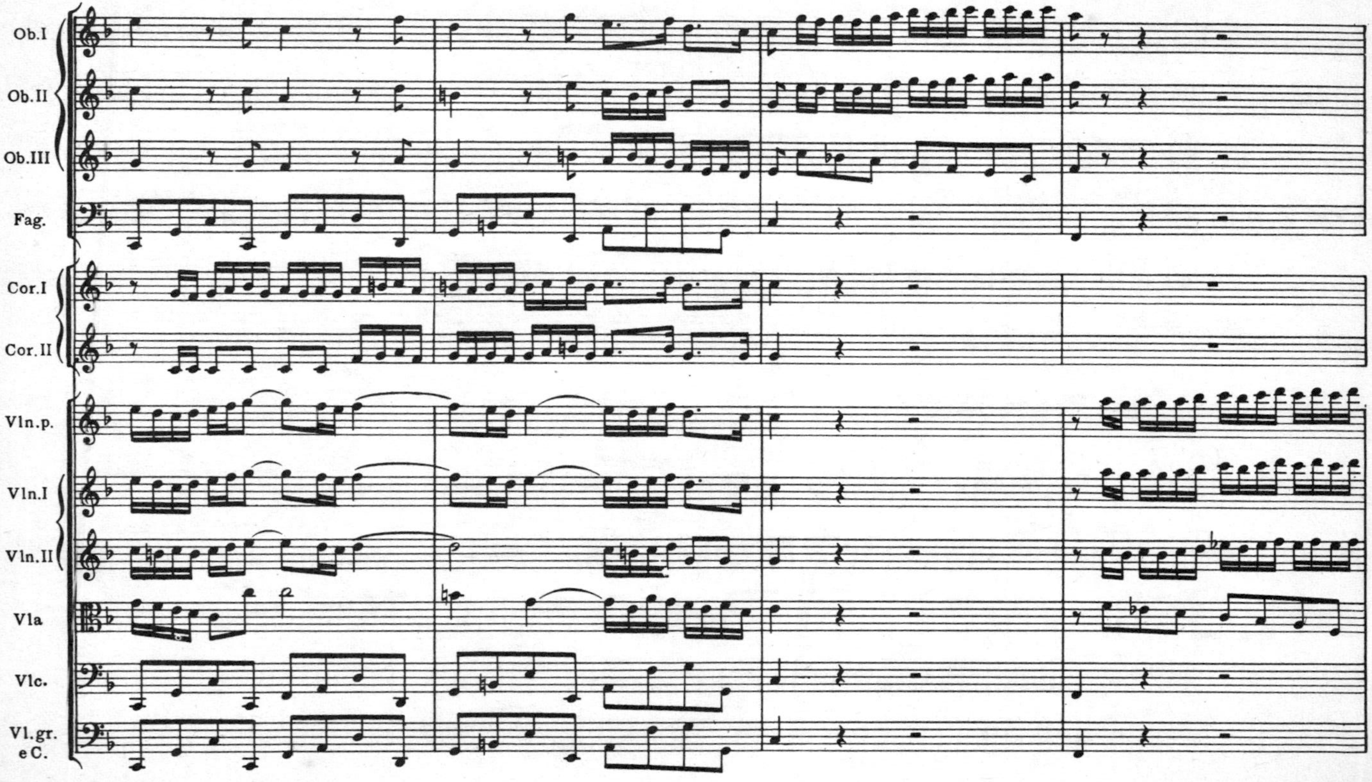
Ob.I
Ob.II
Ob.III
Fag.
Cor.I
Cor.II
Vln.p.
Vln.I
Vln.II
Vla
Vlc.
Vl.gr. e C.

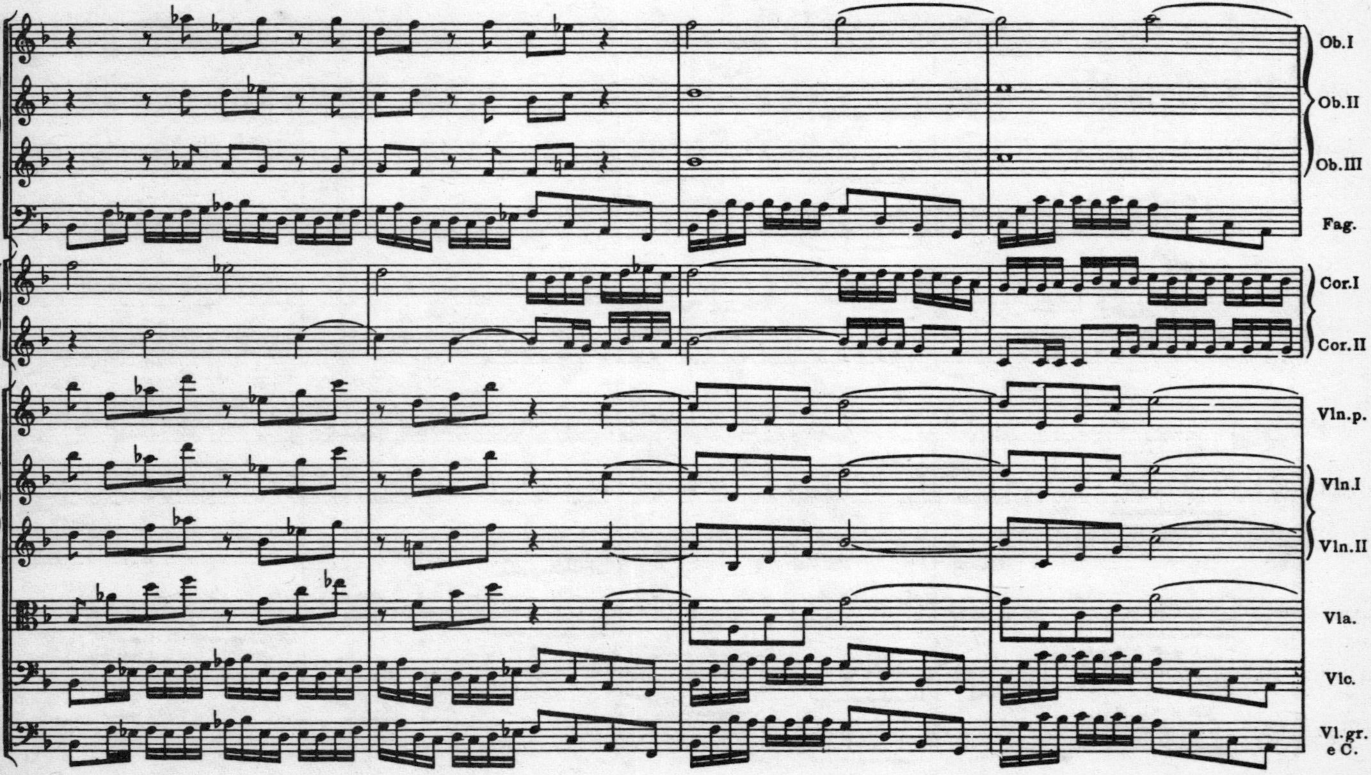
Ob.I
Ob.II
Ob.III
Fag.
Cor.I
Cor.II
Vln.p.
Vln.I
Vln.II
Vla.
Vlc.
Vl.gr. e C.

70
Ob.I
Ob.II
Ob.III
Fag.
Cor.I
Cor.II
Vln.p.
Vln.I
Vln.II
Vla
Vlc.
Vl.gr. e C.
70

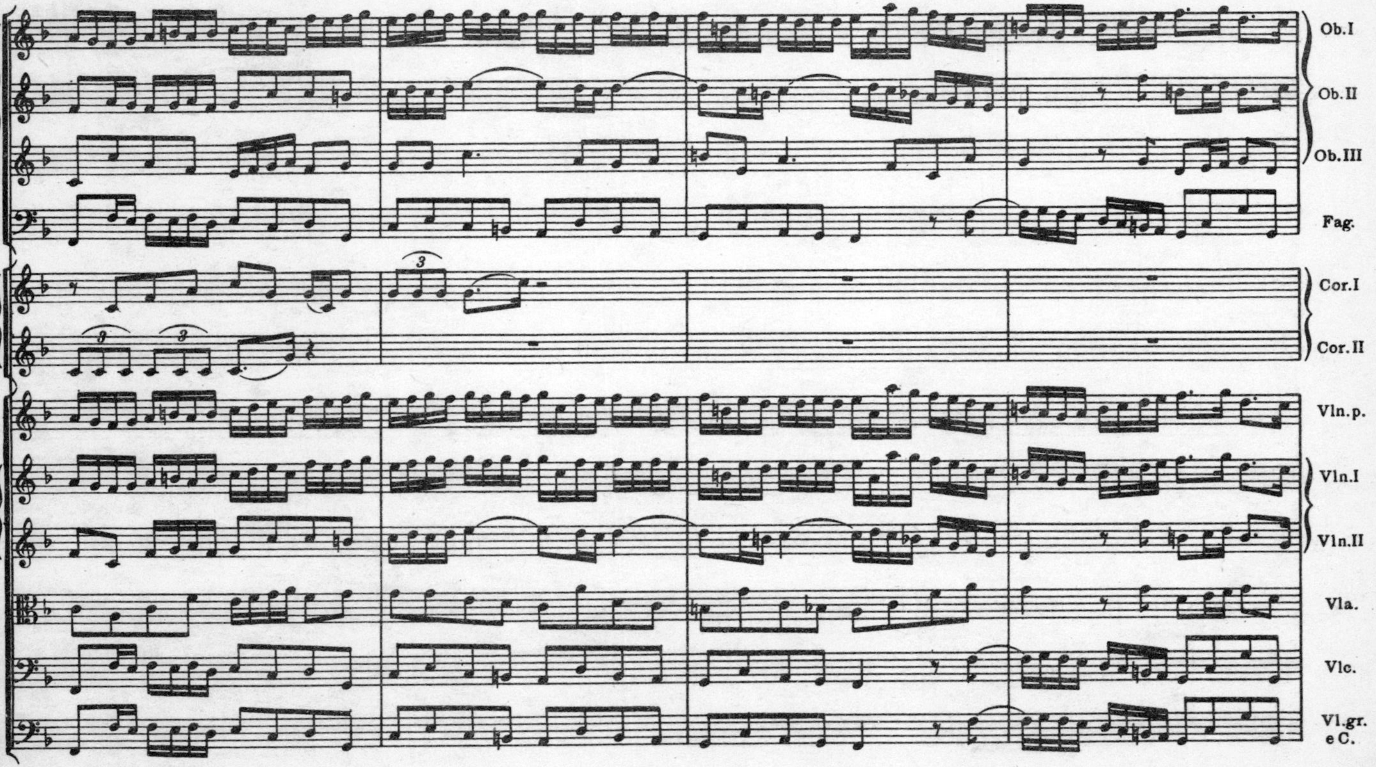
Ob.I
Ob.II
Ob.III
Fag.
Cor.I
Cor.II
Vln.p.
Vln.I
Vln.II
Vla.
Vlc.
Vl.gr. e C.

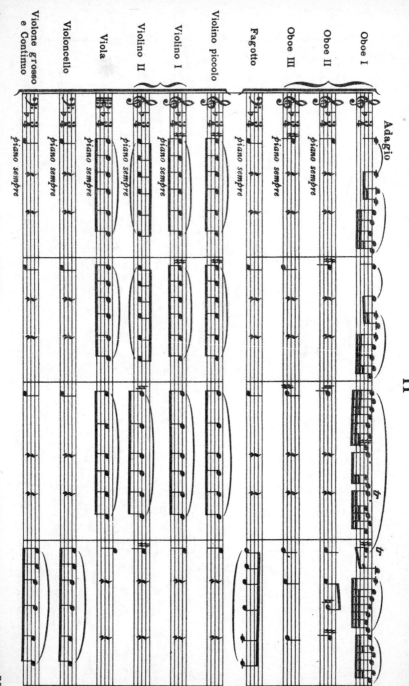

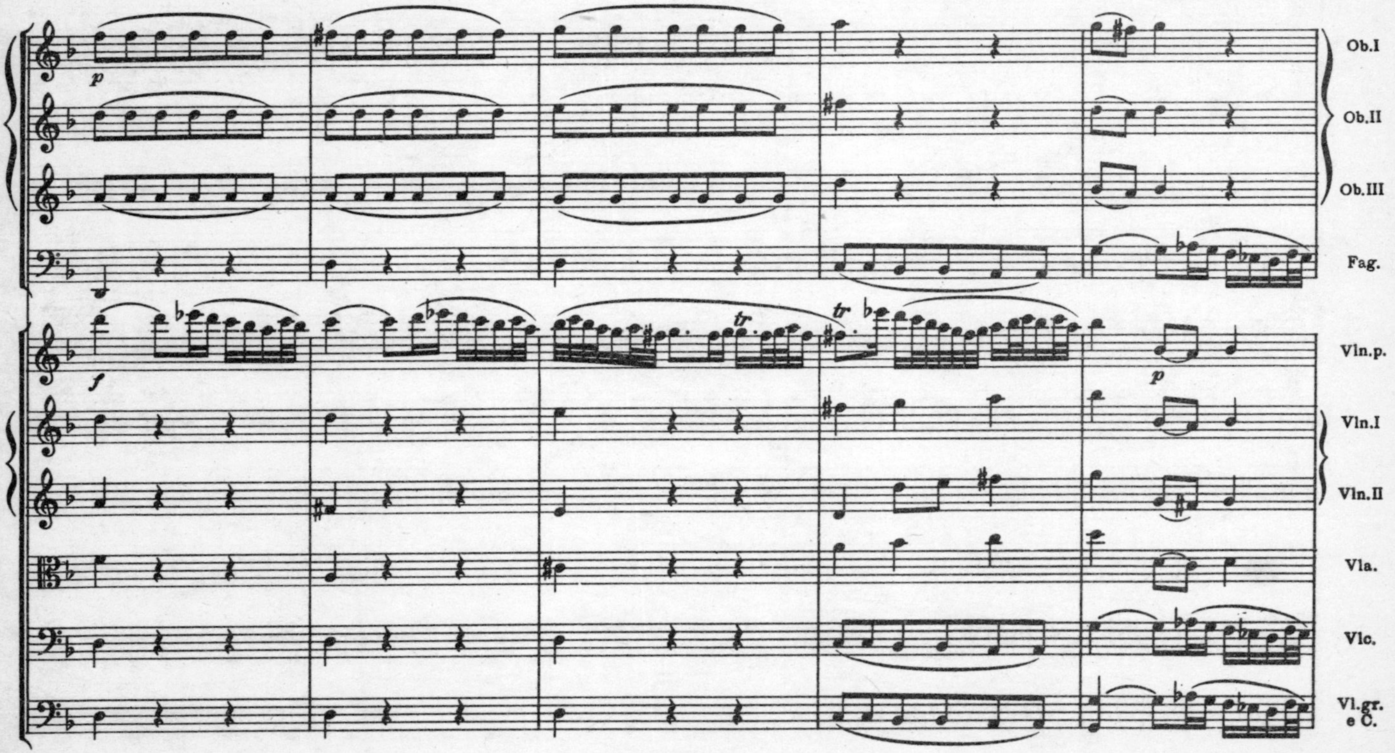

p
Ob.I
Ob.II
Ob.III
Fag.
f
tr
tr
p
Vln.p.
Vln.I
Vln.II
Vla.
Vlc.
Vl.gr.
e C.

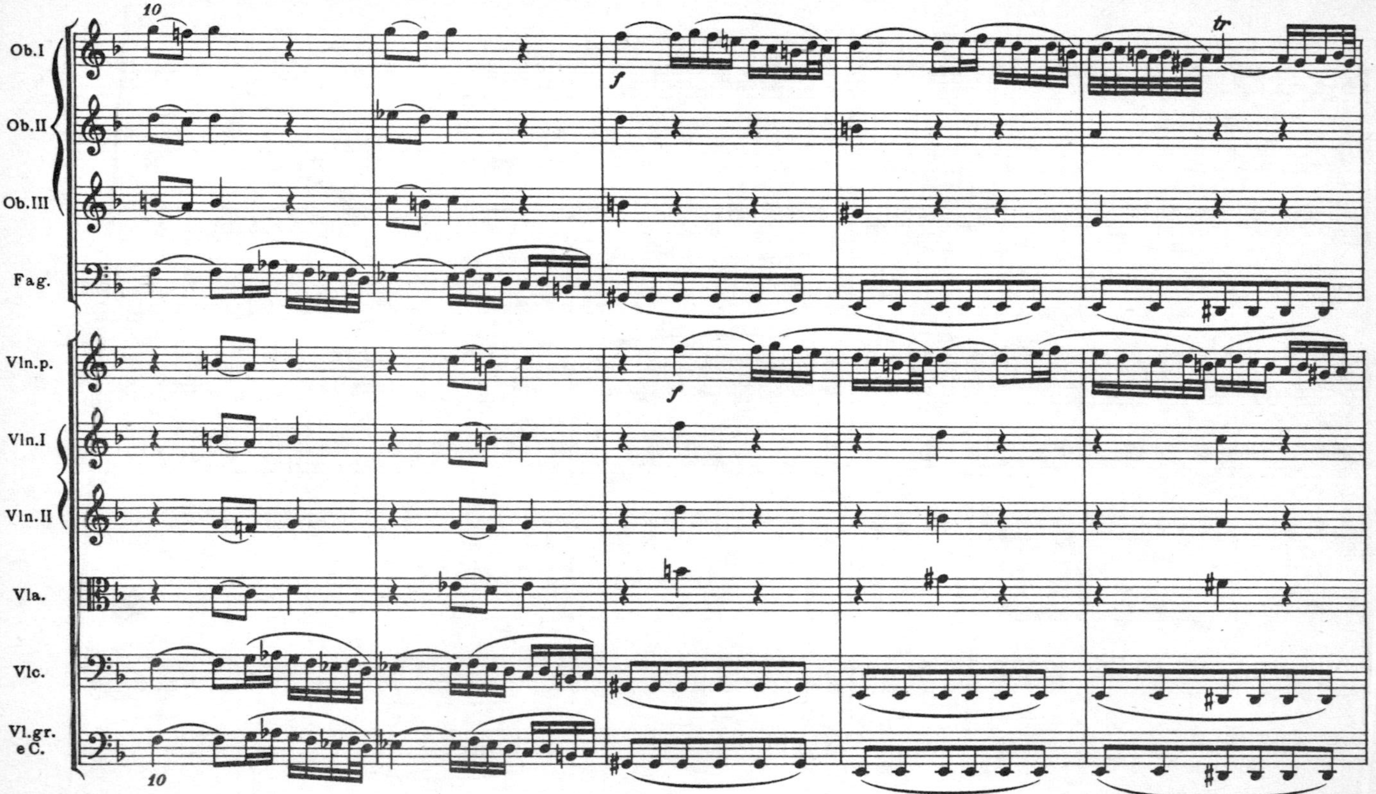
10
Ob.I
Ob.II
Ob.III
Fag.
Vln.p.
Vln.I
Vln.II
Vla.
Vlc.
Vl.gr. e C.
f
tr

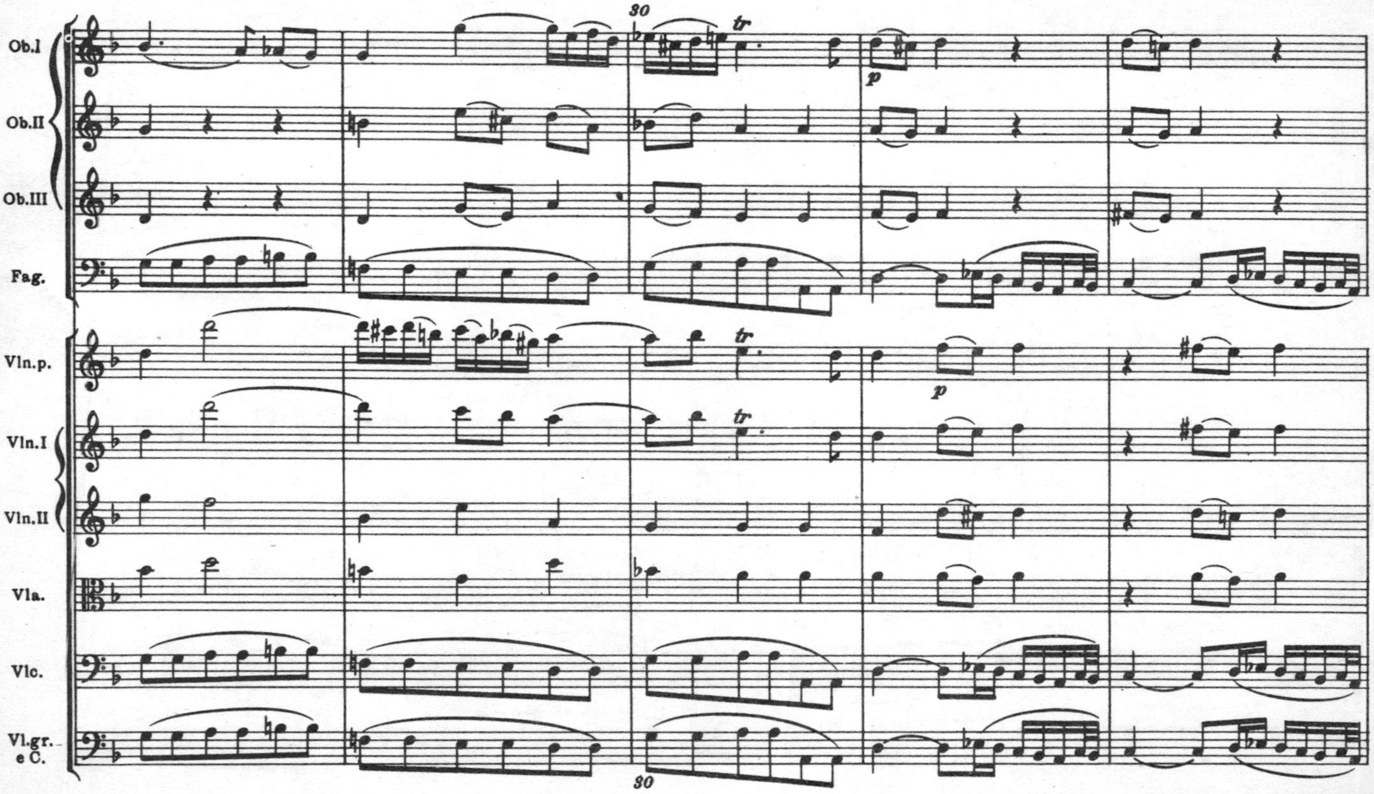
Ob.I
Ob.II
Ob.III
Fag.
Vln.p.
Vln.I
Vln.II
Vla.
Vlc.
Vl.gr. e C.
30
tr
p
30

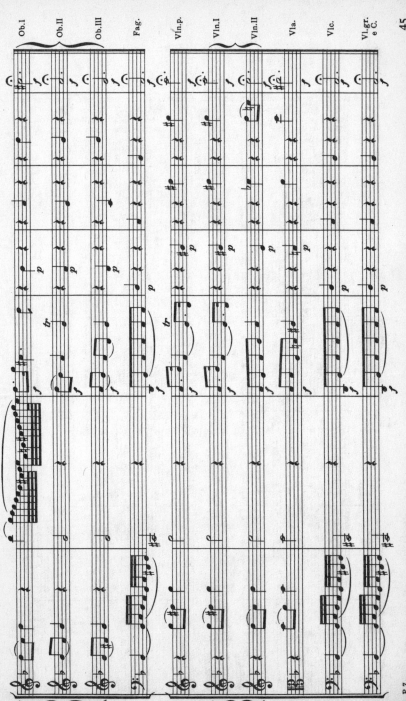

III

Allegro

Oboe I
Oboe II
Oboe III
Fagotto
Corno I (actual sounds)
Corno II (actual sounds)
Violino piccolo
Violino I
Violino II
Viola
Violoncello
Violone grosso e Continuo

46

P.7

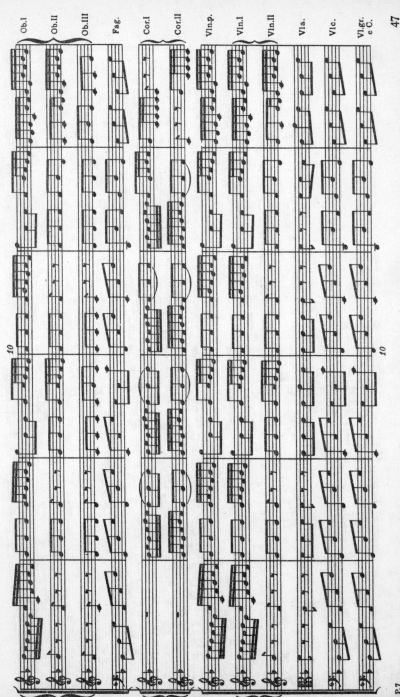

Ob.I
Ob.II
Ob.III
Fag.
Cor.I
Cor.II
Vln.p.
Vln.I
Vln.II
Vla.
Vlc.
Vl.gr. e C.
sempre p
sempre p
tr

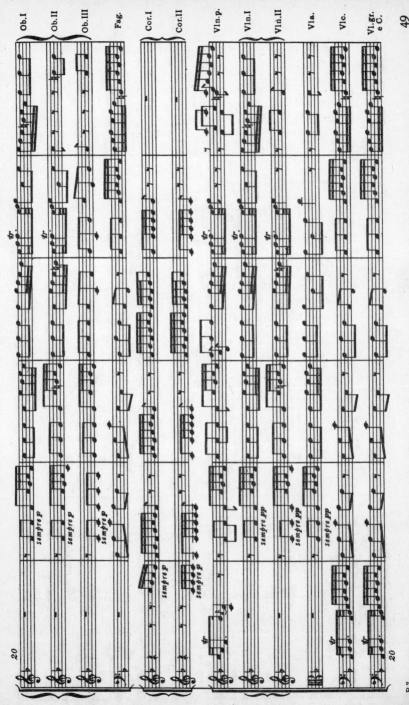

Ob.I
Ob.II
Ob.III
Fag.
Cor.I
Cor.II
Vln.p.
Vln.I
Vln.II
Vla.
Vlc.
Vl.gr. e C.
30
30

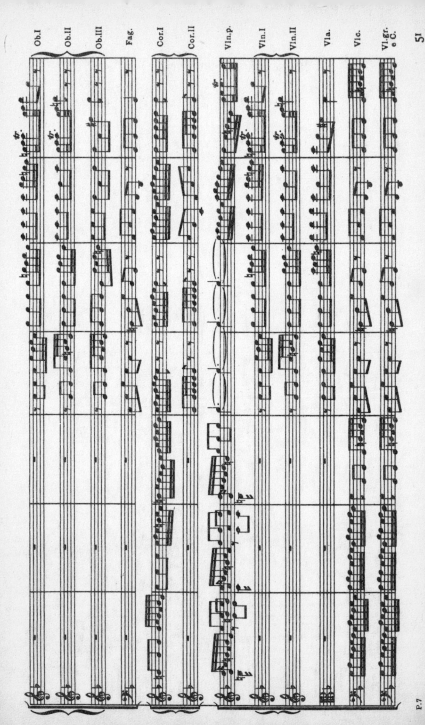

40
Ob.I
Ob.II
Ob.III
Fag.
Cor.I
Cor.II
Vln.p.
Vln.I
Vln.II
Vla.
Vlc.
Vl.gr. e C.
f
40

50
Ob.I
Ob.II
Ob.III
Fag.
Cor.I
Cor.II
Vln.p.
Vln.I
Vln.II
Vla.
Vlc.
Vl.gr.
e C.
50

Ob. I
Ob. II
Ob. III
Fag.
Cor. I
Cor. II
Vln. p.
Vln. I
Vln. II
Vla.
Vlc.
Vl. gr. e C.
p
tr

70
Ob.I
Ob.II
Ob.III
Fag
Cor.I
Cor.II
Vln.p.
Vln.I
Vln.II
Vla.
Vlc.
Vl.gr. e C.
70

Ob.I
Ob.II
Ob.III
Fag.
Cor.I
Cor.II
Vln.p.
Vln.I
Vln.II
Vla.
Vlc.
Vl.gr. e C.
80
tr
p

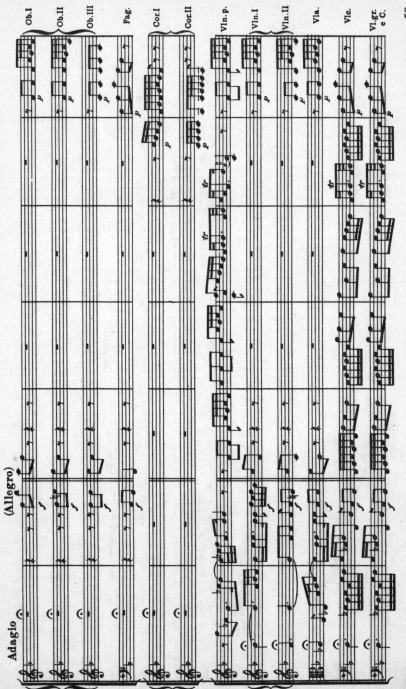

90
Ob.I
Ob.II
Ob.III
Fag.
Cor.I
Cor.II
Vln. p.
Vln.I
Vln.II
Vla.
Vlc.
Vl.gr. e C.
(tr)
(tr)
tr.
tr.
tr
90

100
Ob.I
Ob.II
Ob.III
Fag.
Cor.I
Cor.II
Vln.p.
Vln.I
Vln.II
Vla.
Vlc.
Vl.gr.
e.C.
100

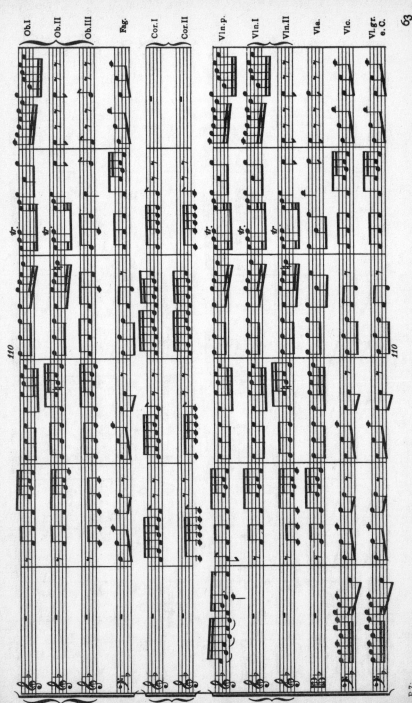

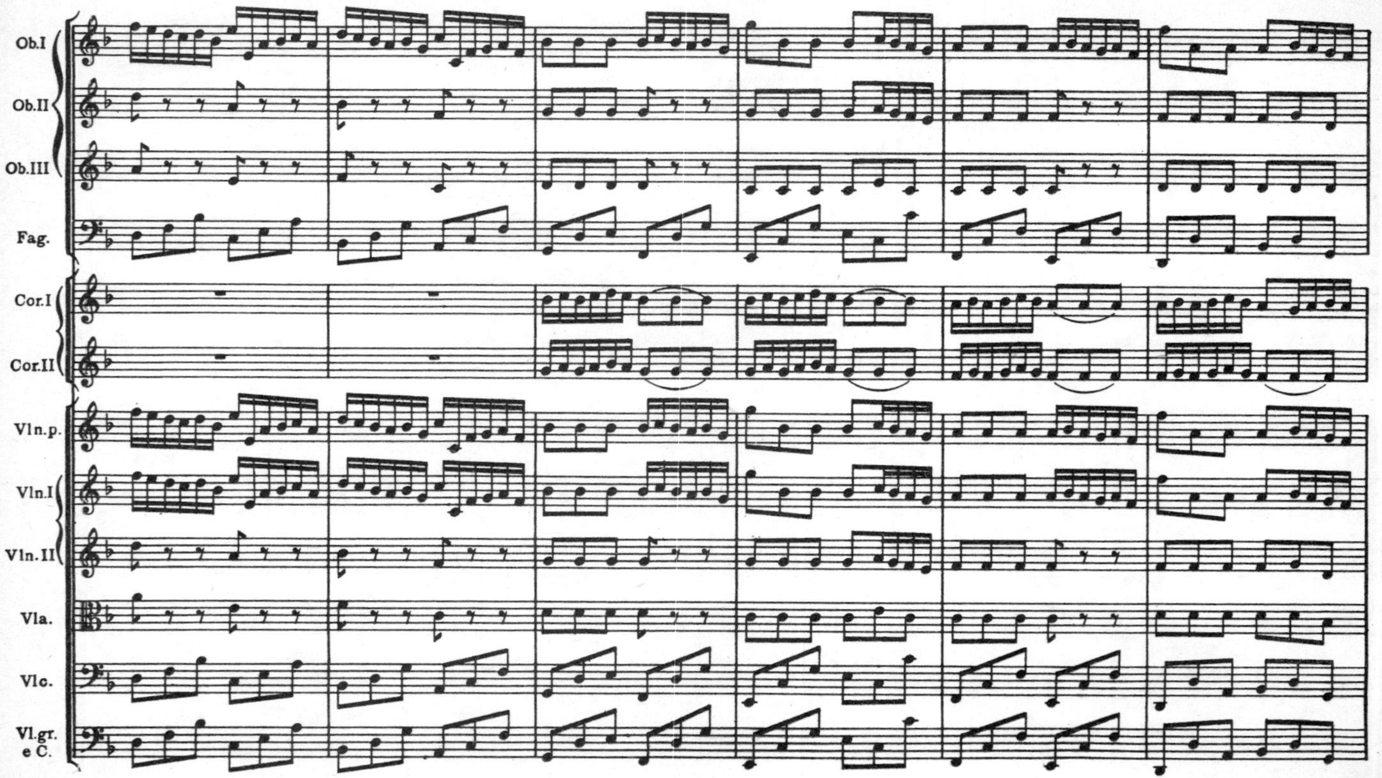
Ob.I
Ob.II
Ob.III
Fag.
Cor.I
Cor.II
Vln.p.
Vln.I
Vln.II
Vla.
Vlc.
Vl.gr. e C.

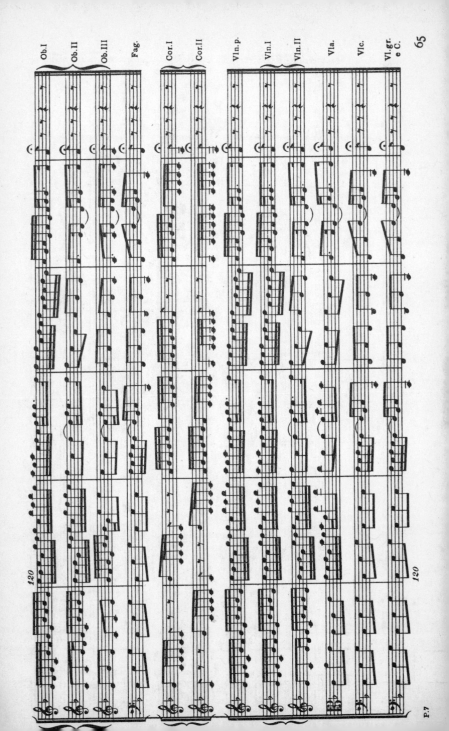

MENUETTO

IV

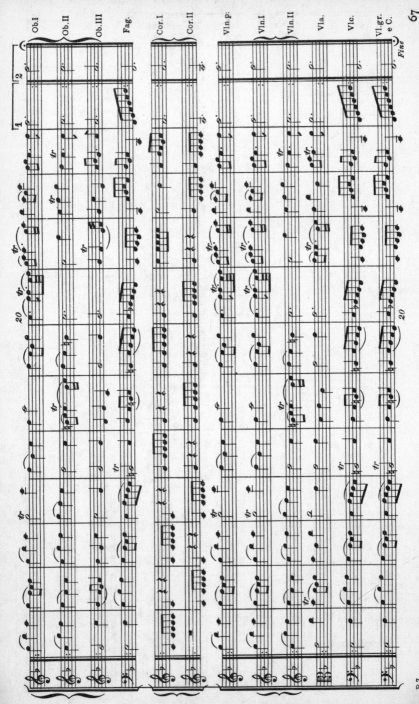

TRIO I a. 2 Oboi e Fagotto

Menuetto da Capo, e poi la Polacca

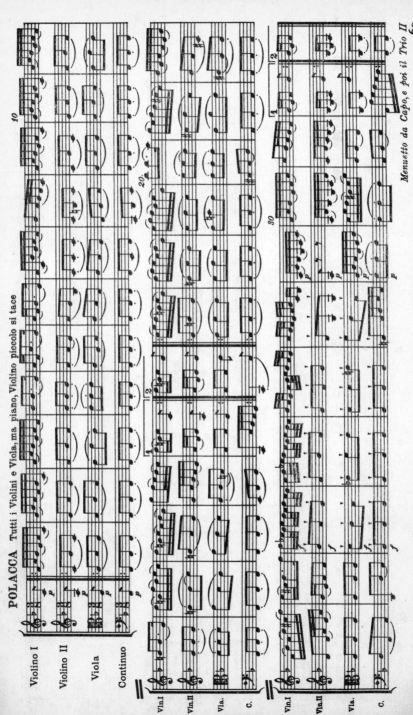

POLACCA Tutti i Violini e Viola, ma piano, Violino piccolo si tace

Violino I

Violino II

Viola

Continuo

Menuetto da Capo, e poi il Trio II

69

P.7

TRIO II

Corno I
(actual sounds)

Corno II
(actual sounds)

Tutti le
Oboi

Cor.I

Cor.II

Ob.

Cor.I

Cor.II

Ob.

Menuetto da Capo sino alla Fine

70

P.7

Brandenburg Concerto No. 2

I

[Allegro]

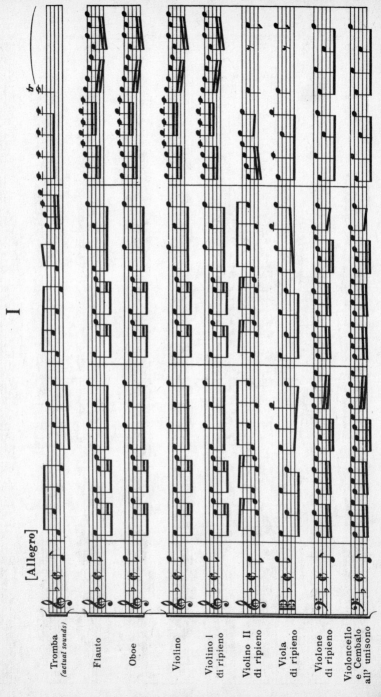

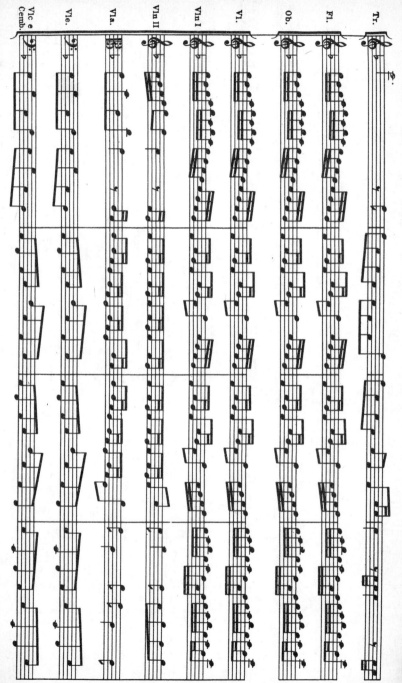

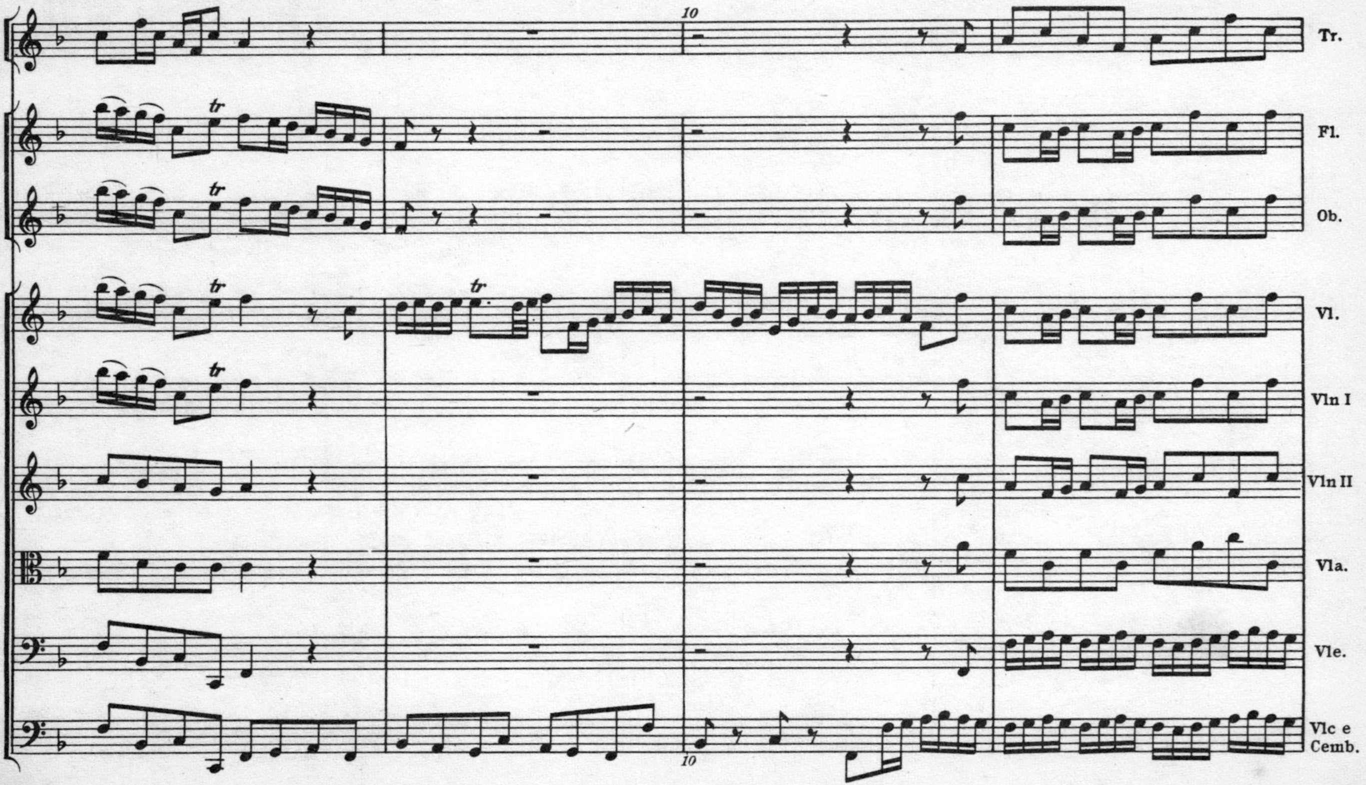
10
Tr.
Fl.
Ob.
Vl.
Vln I
Vln II
Vla.
Vle.
Vlc e
Cemb.
10

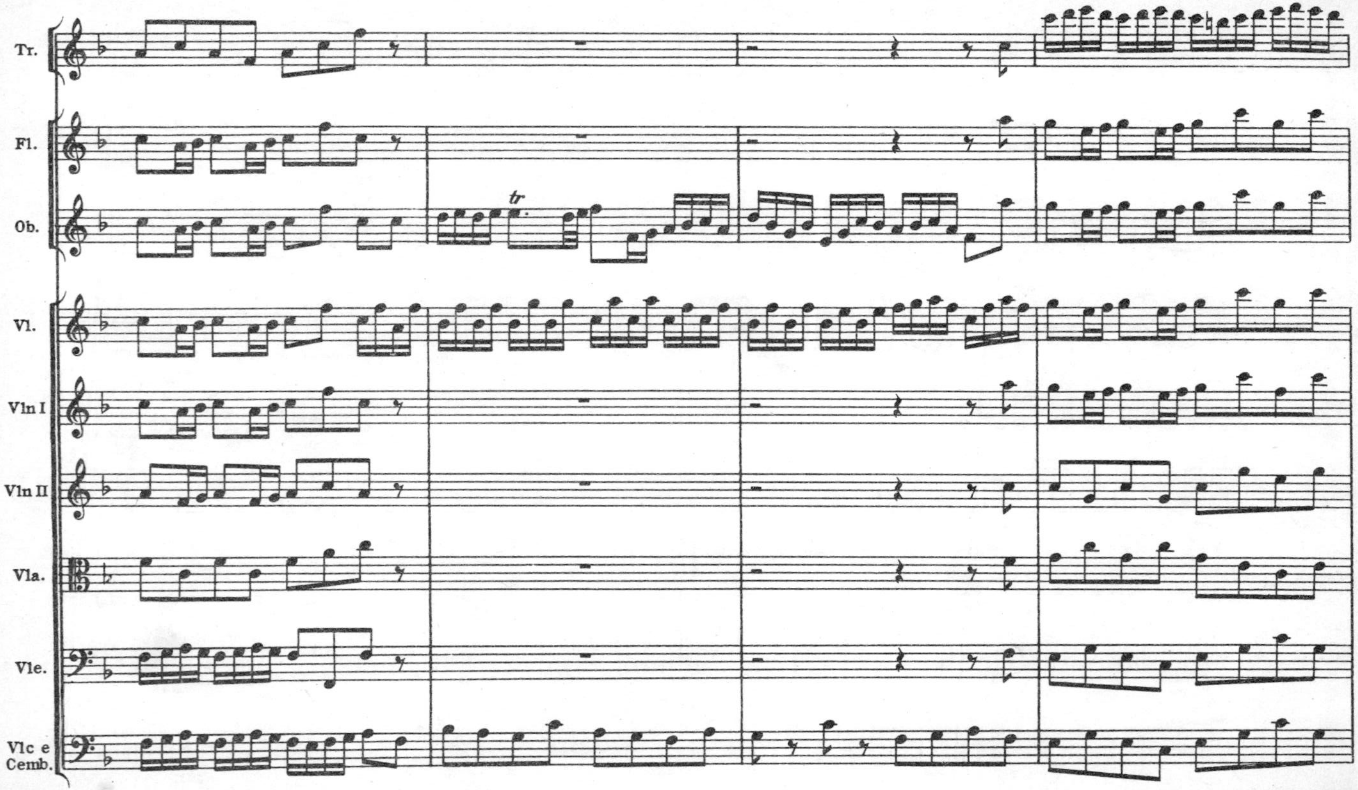
Tr.
Fl.
Ob.
tr
Vl.
Vln I
Vln II
Vla.
Vle.
Vlc e Cemb.

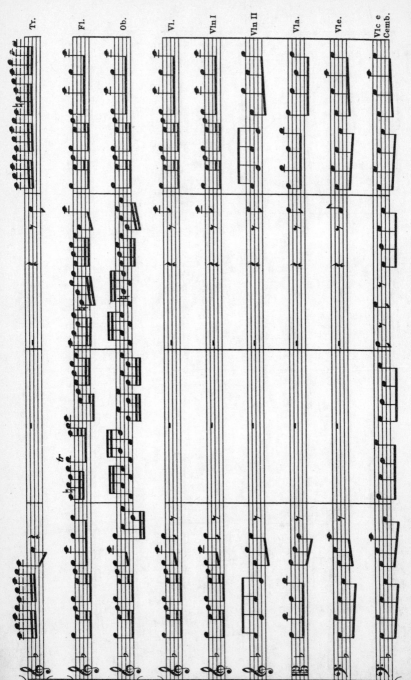

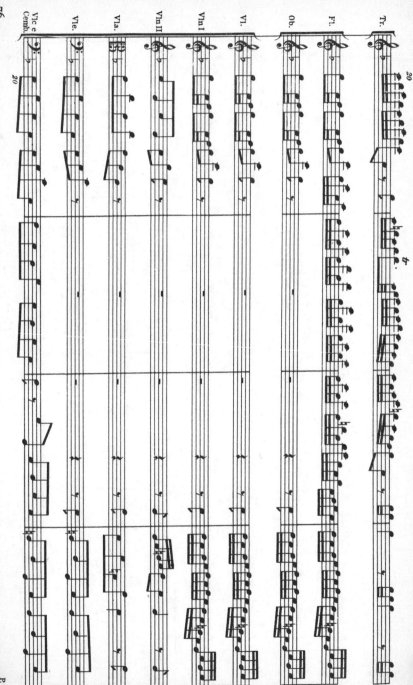

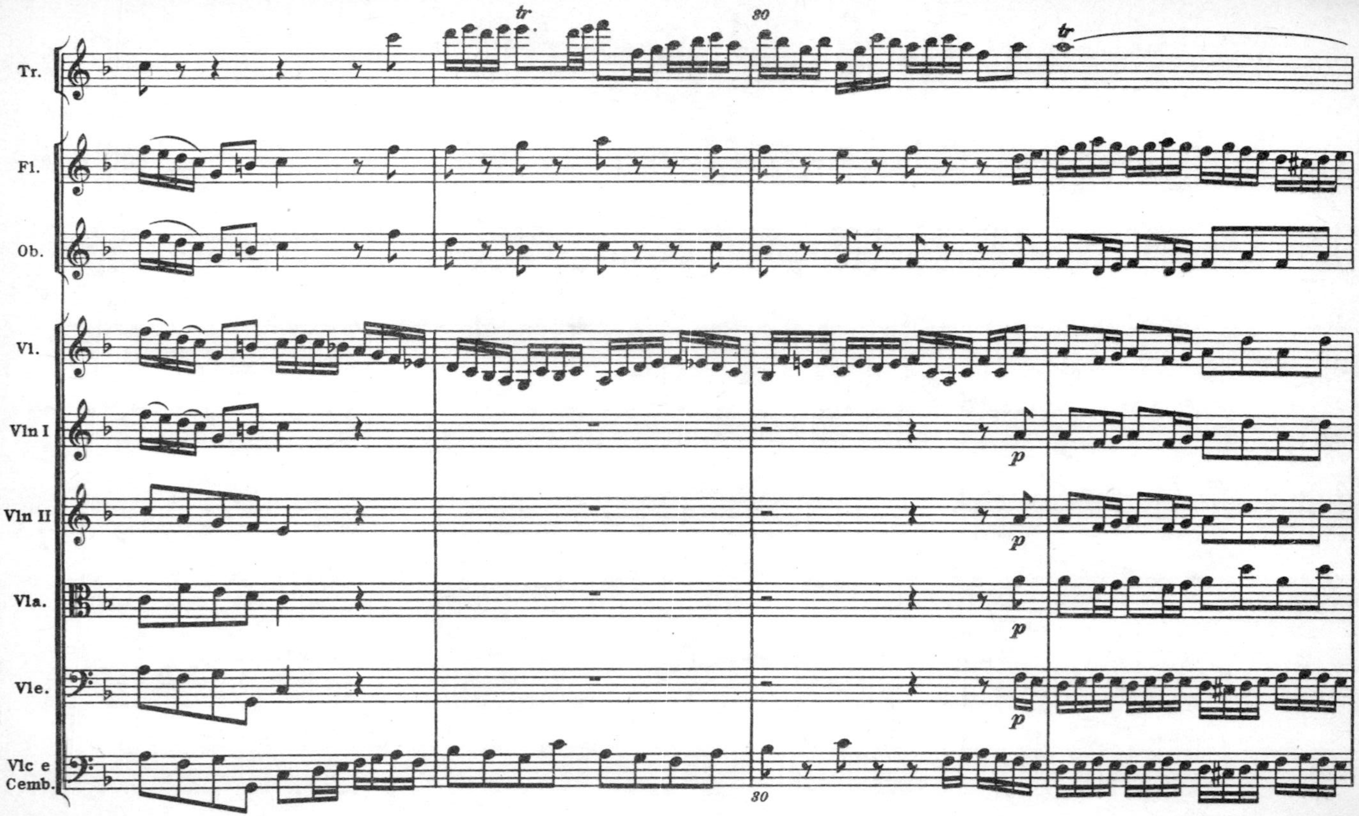

Tr.
Fl.
Ob.
Vl.
Vln I
Vln II
Vla.
Vle.
Vlc e Cemb.
tr
80
p

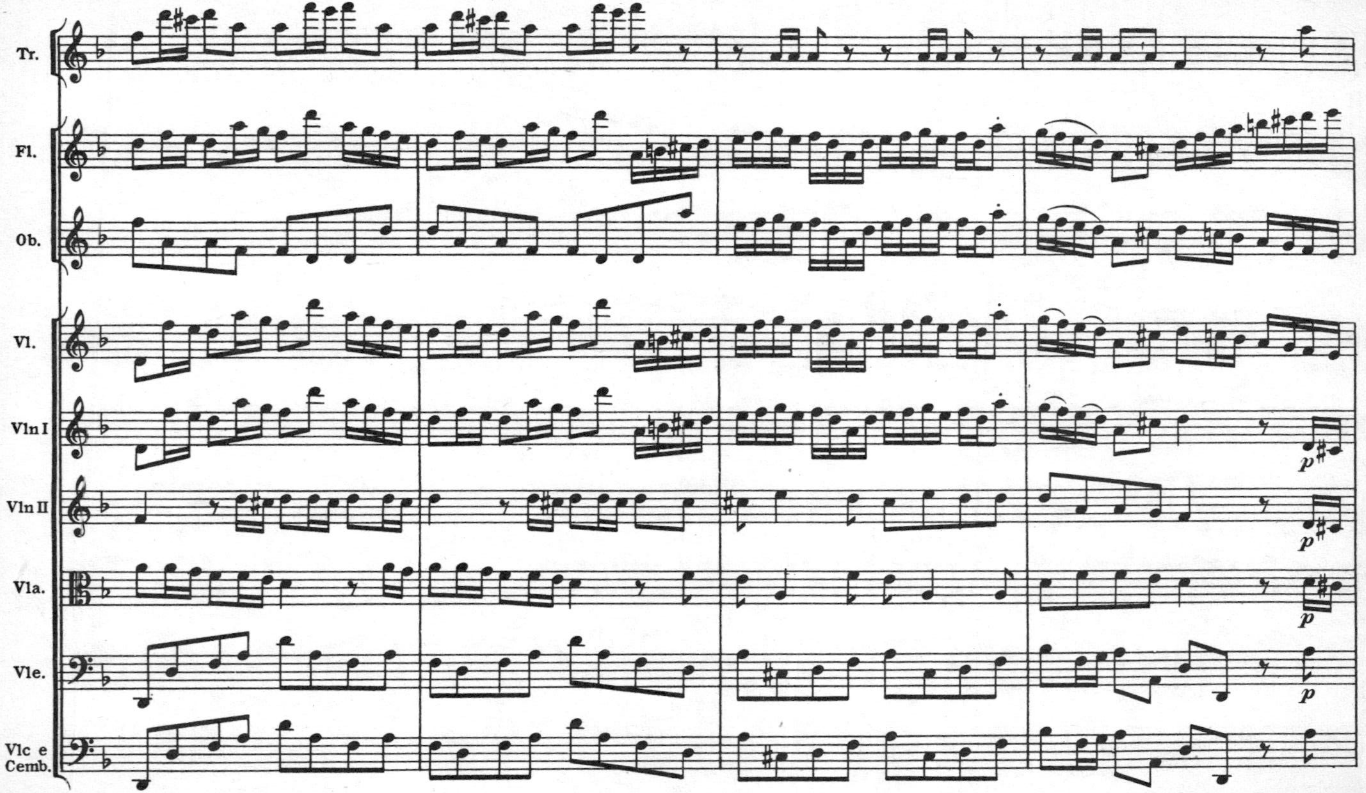
Tr.
Fl.
Ob.
Vl.
Vln I
Vln II
Vla.
Vle.
Vlc e Cemb.
p
p
p
p

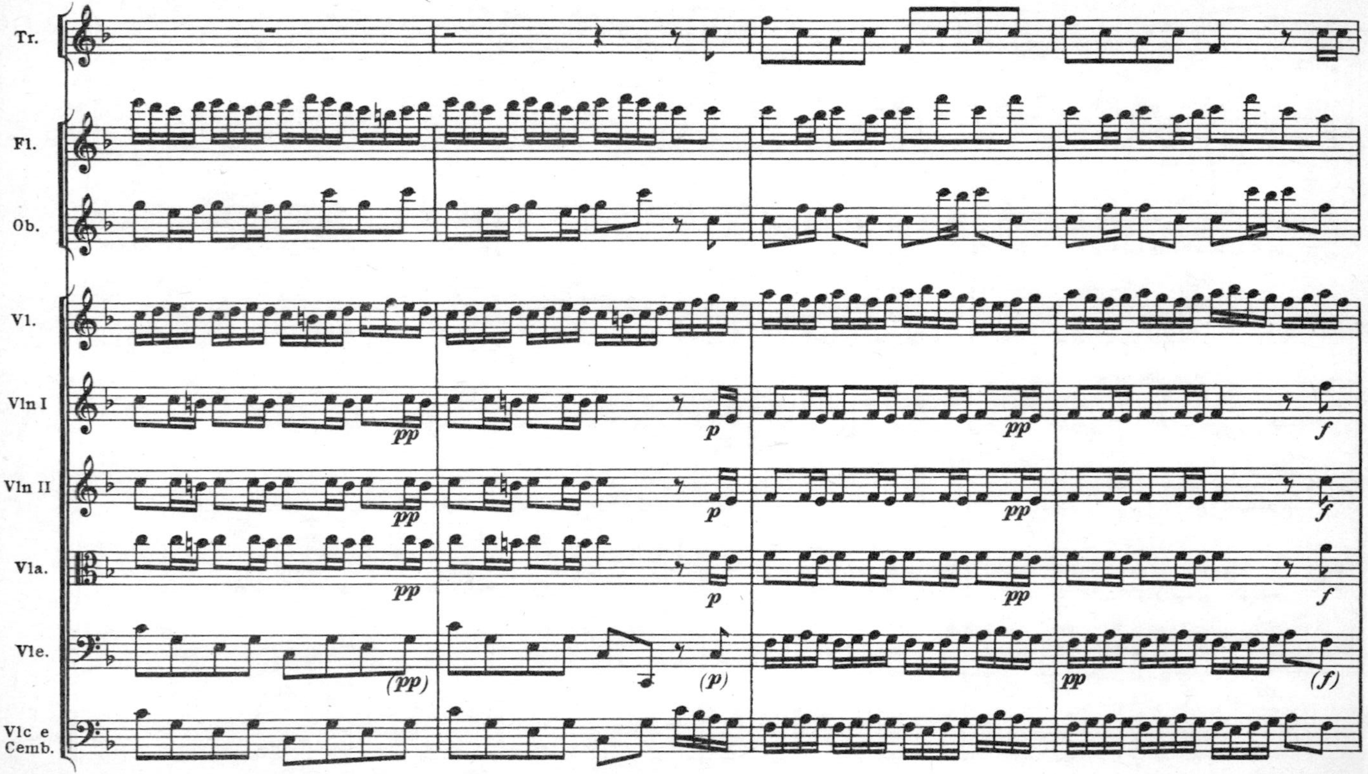
Tr.
Fl.
Ob.
Vl.
Vln I
Vln II
Vla.
Vle.
Vlc e Cemb.
pp
p
f
(pp)
(p)
(f)

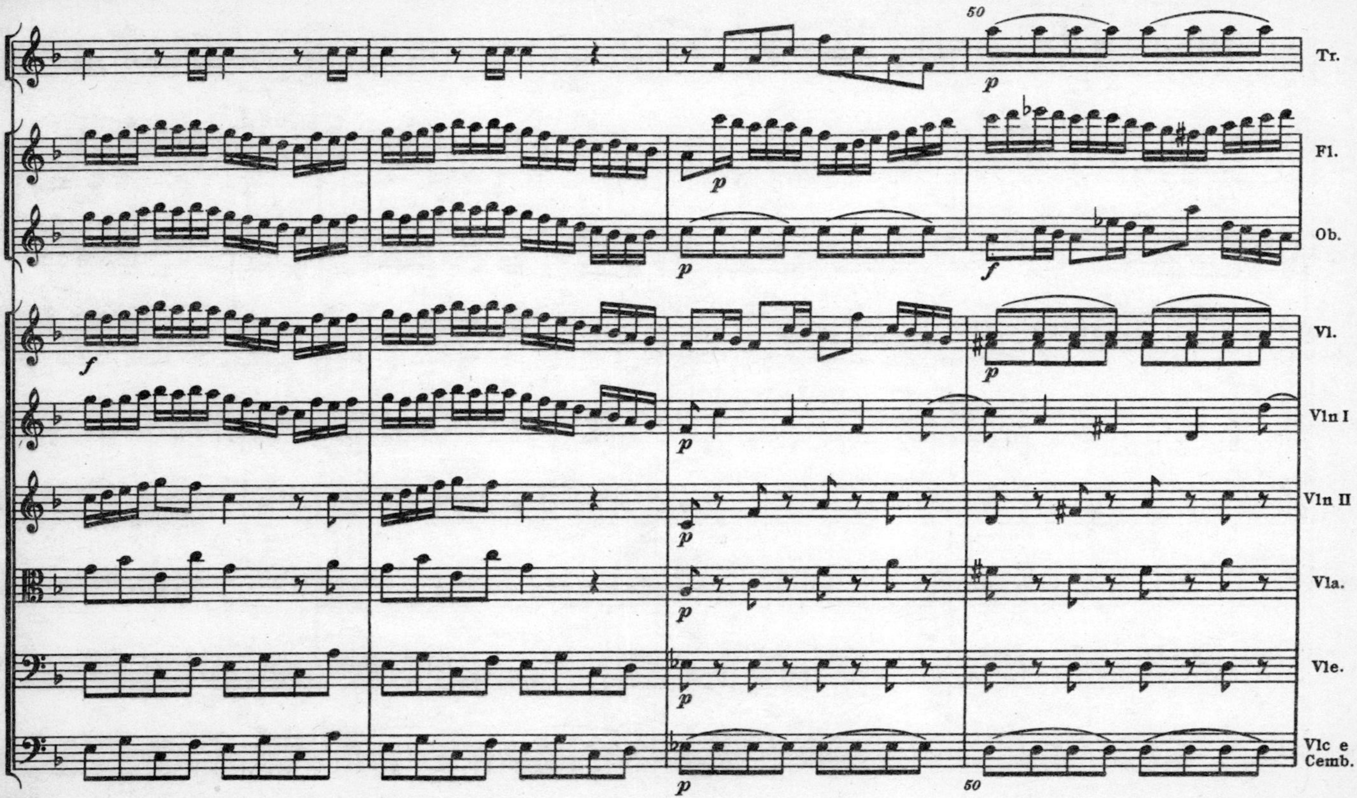

50
Tr.
p
Fl.
p
Ob.
p
f
Vl.
f
p
Vln I
p
Vln II
p
Vla.
p
Vle.
p
Vlc e
Cemb.
p
50

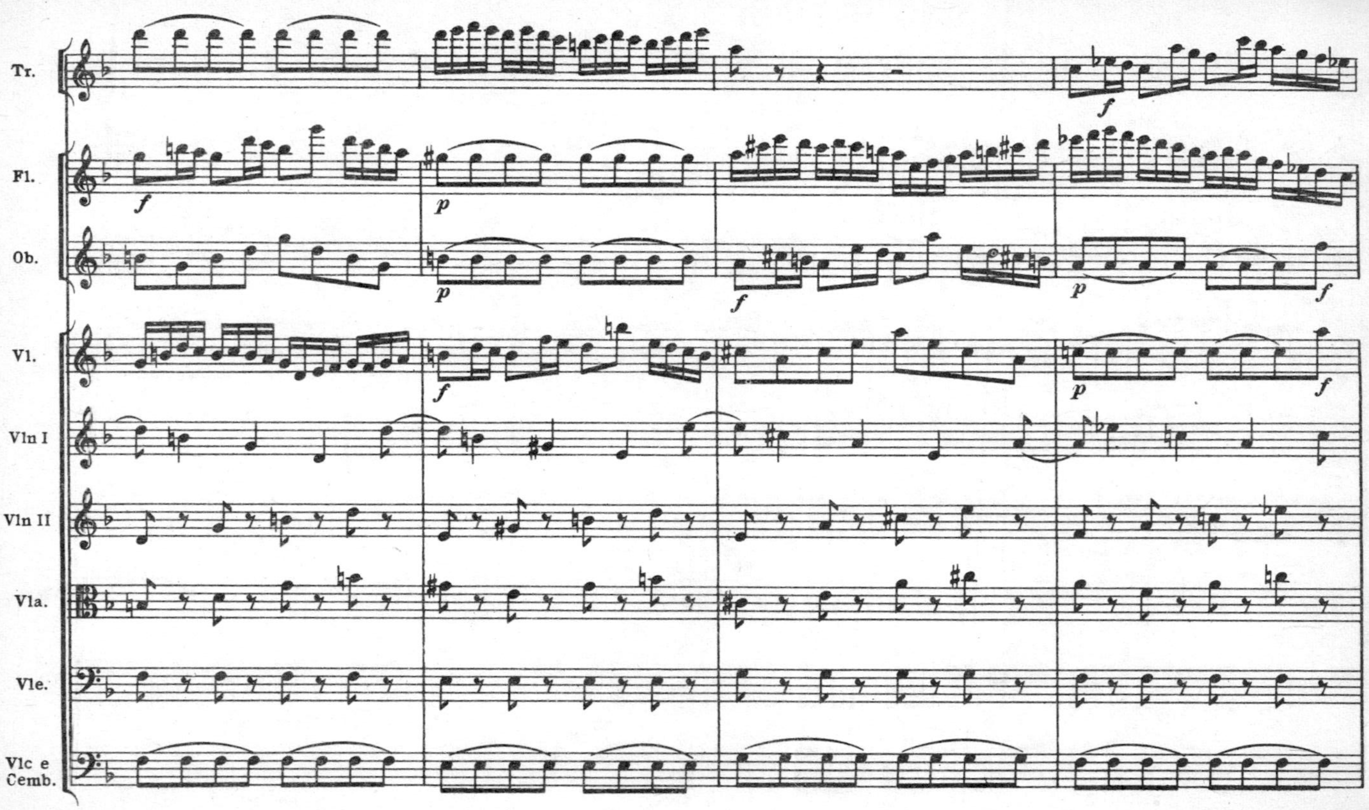
Tr.
Fl.
Ob.
Vl.
Vln I
Vln II
Vla.
Vle.
Vlc e Cemb.
f
p
f
p
p
f
p
f
f
p
f
f
p
f

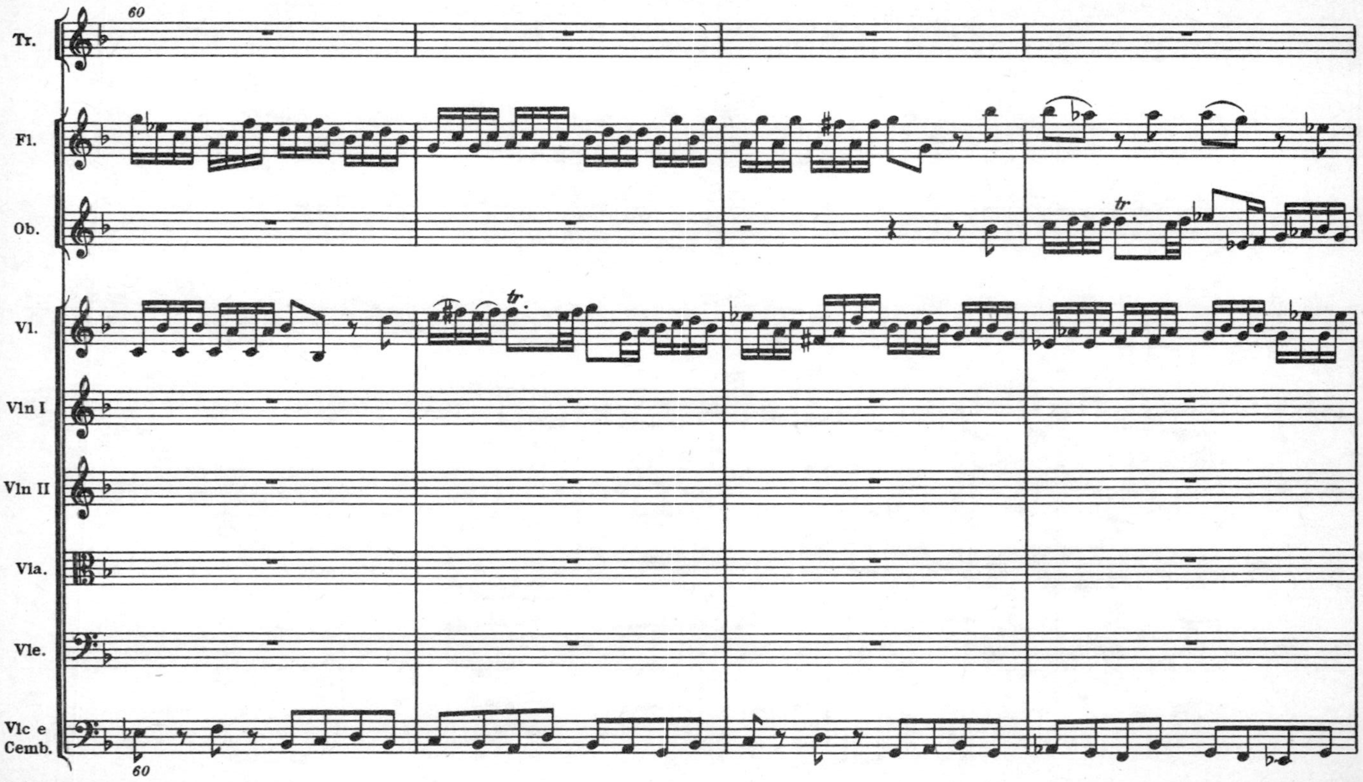
60
Tr.
Fl.
Ob.
tr
Vl.
tr
Vln I
Vln II
Vla.
Vle.
Vlc e
Cemb.
60

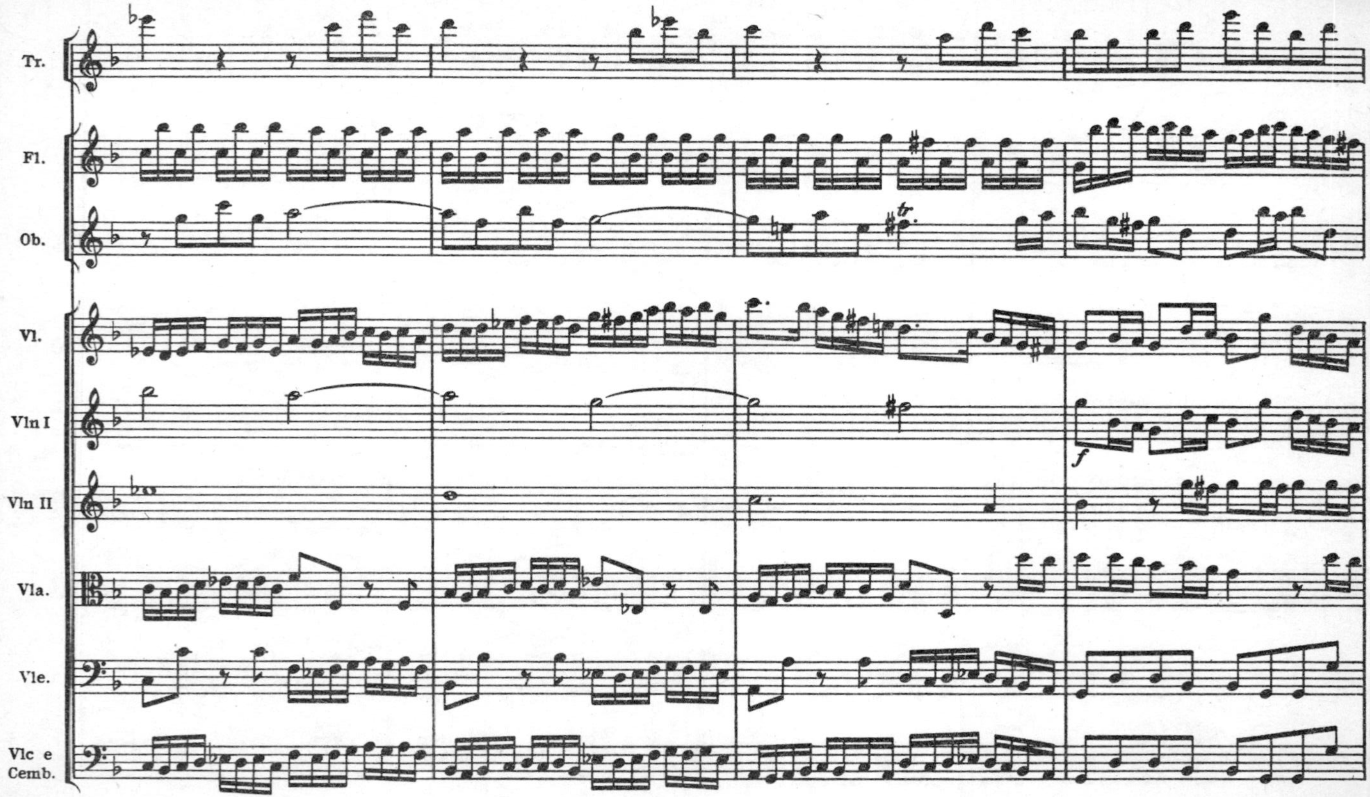
Tr.
Fl.
Ob.
tr
Vl.
Vln I
f
Vln II
Vla.
Vle.
Vlc e
Cemb.

92

P 7

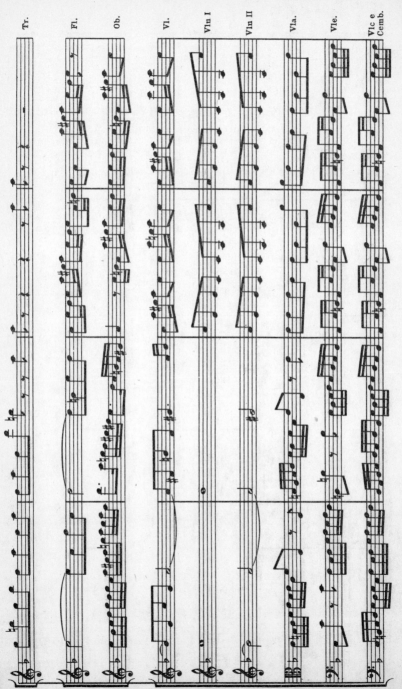

100
Tr.
Fl.
Ob.
Vl.
Vln I
Vln II
Vla.
Vle.
Vlc e
Cemb.
tr
tasto solo
accomp.
6
100

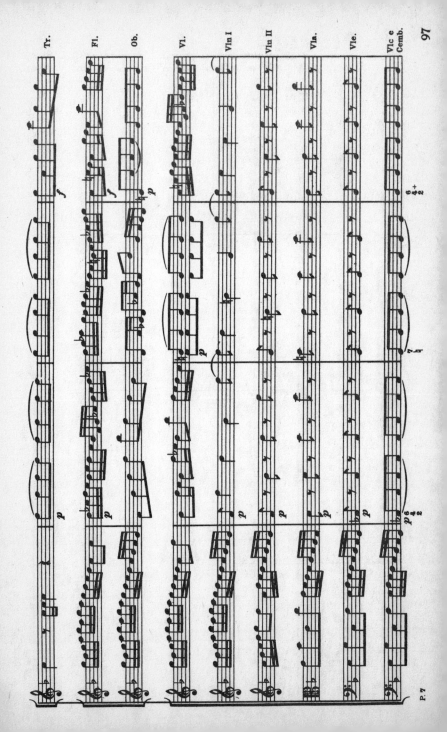

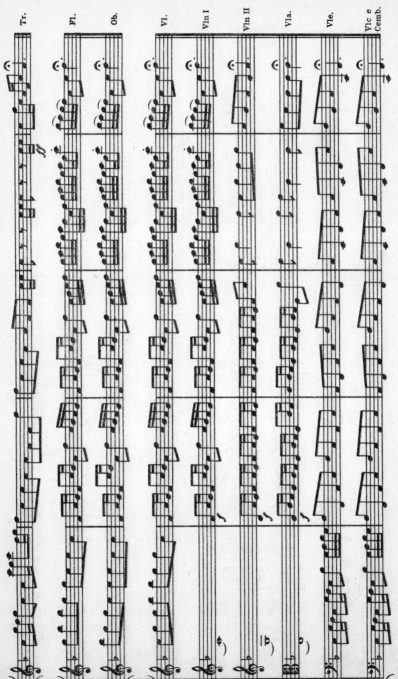

II

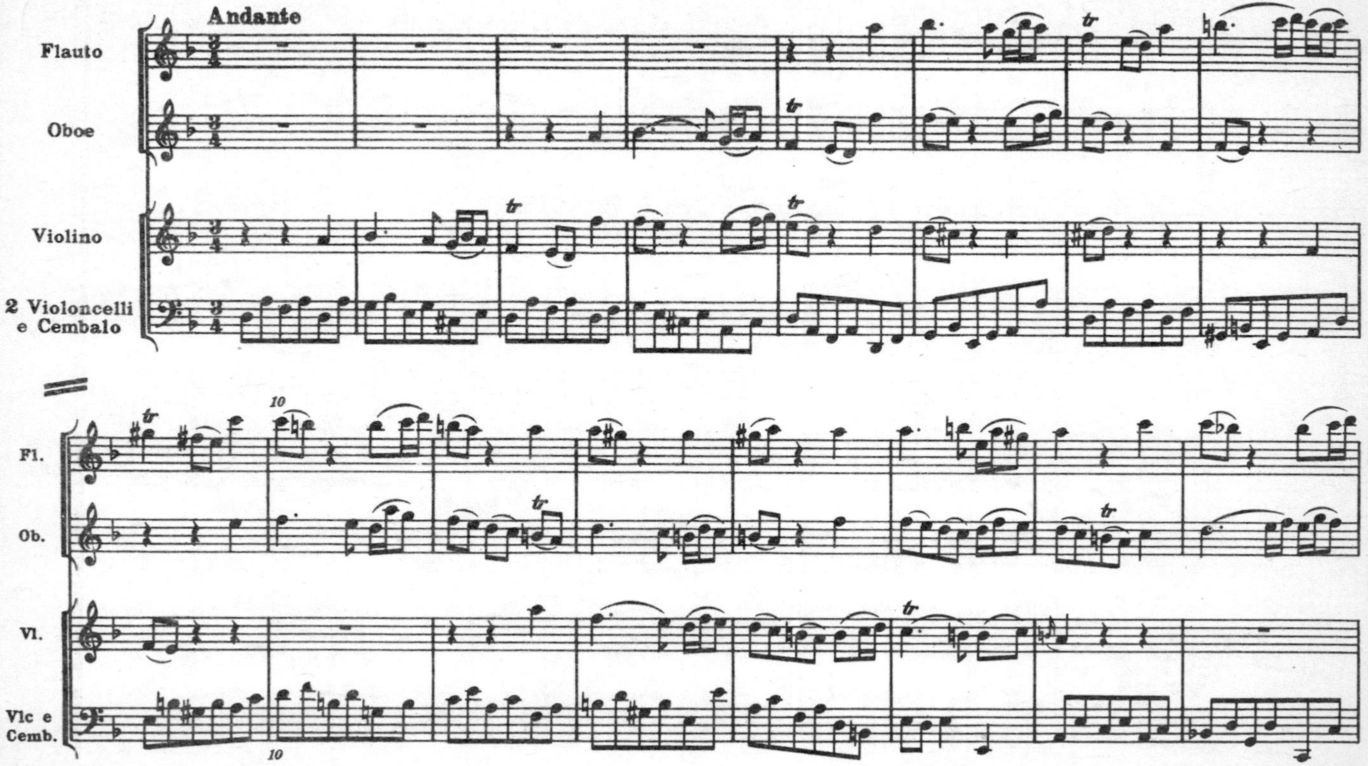
Andante
Flauto
Oboe
Violino
2 Violoncelli e Cembalo
tr
10
Fl.
Ob.
Vl.
Vlc e Cemb.

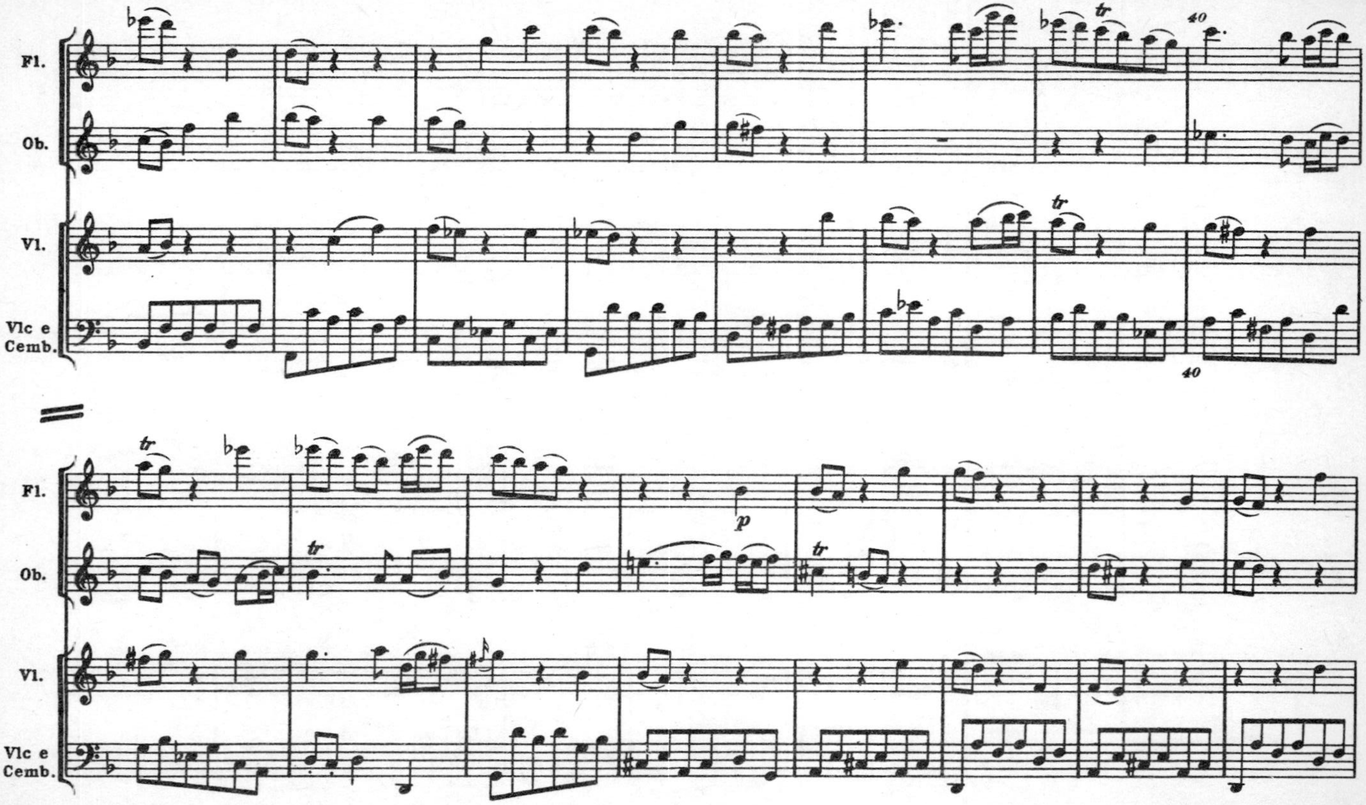
Fl.
Ob.
Vl.
Vlc e Cemb.
tr
40
p
Fl.
Ob.
Vl.
Vlc e Cemb.

III

Allegro assai

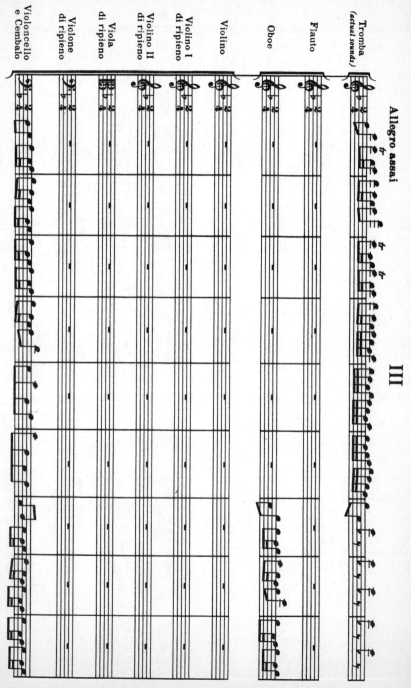

Tromba
(actual sounds.)

Oboe

Flauto

Violino

Violino I
di ripieno

Violino II
di ripieno

Viola
di ripieno

Violone
di ripieno

Violoncello
e Cembalo

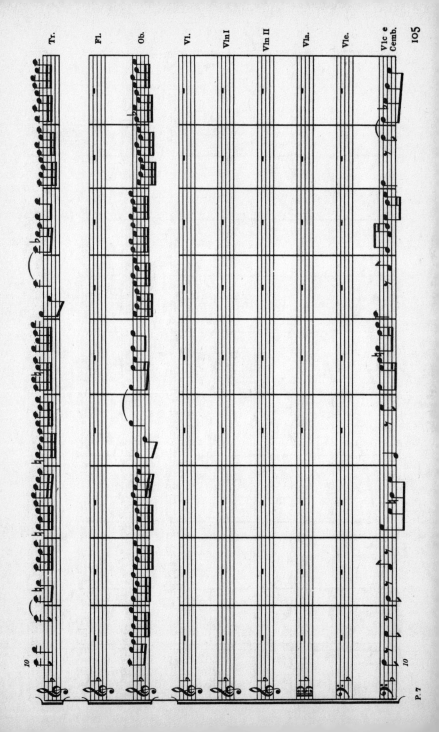

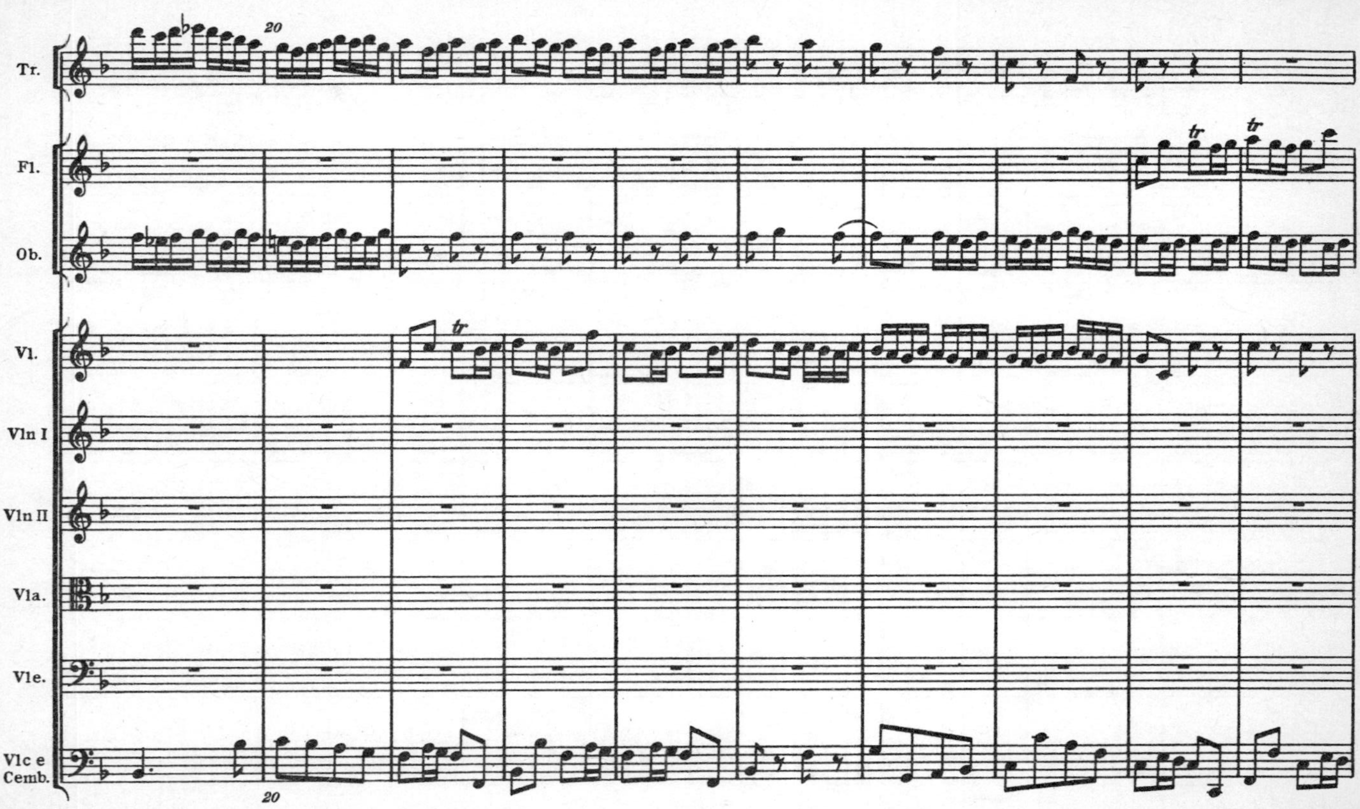
Tr.
Fl.
Ob.
Vl.
Vln I
Vln II
Vla.
Vle.
Vlc e Cemb.
20
tr
tr
tr
20

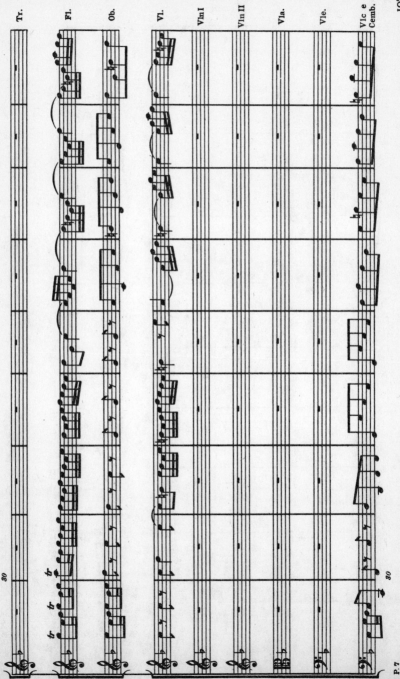

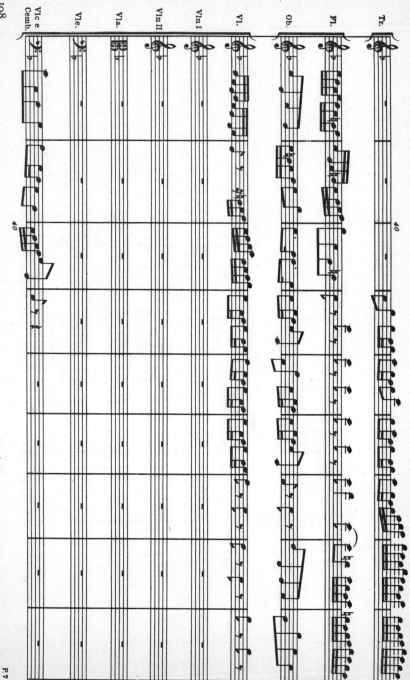

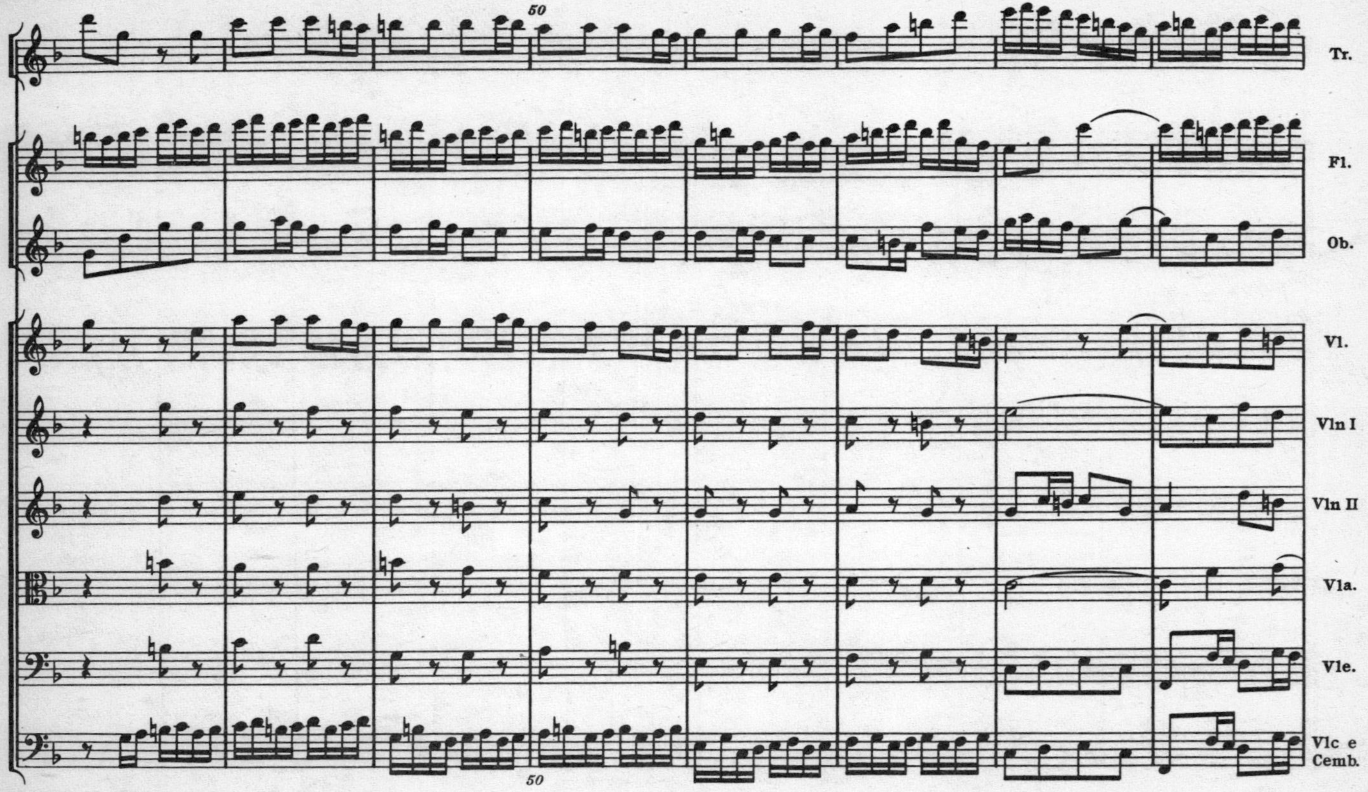
50
Tr.
Fl.
Ob.
Vl.
Vln I
Vln II
Vla.
Vle.
Vlc e Cemb.
50

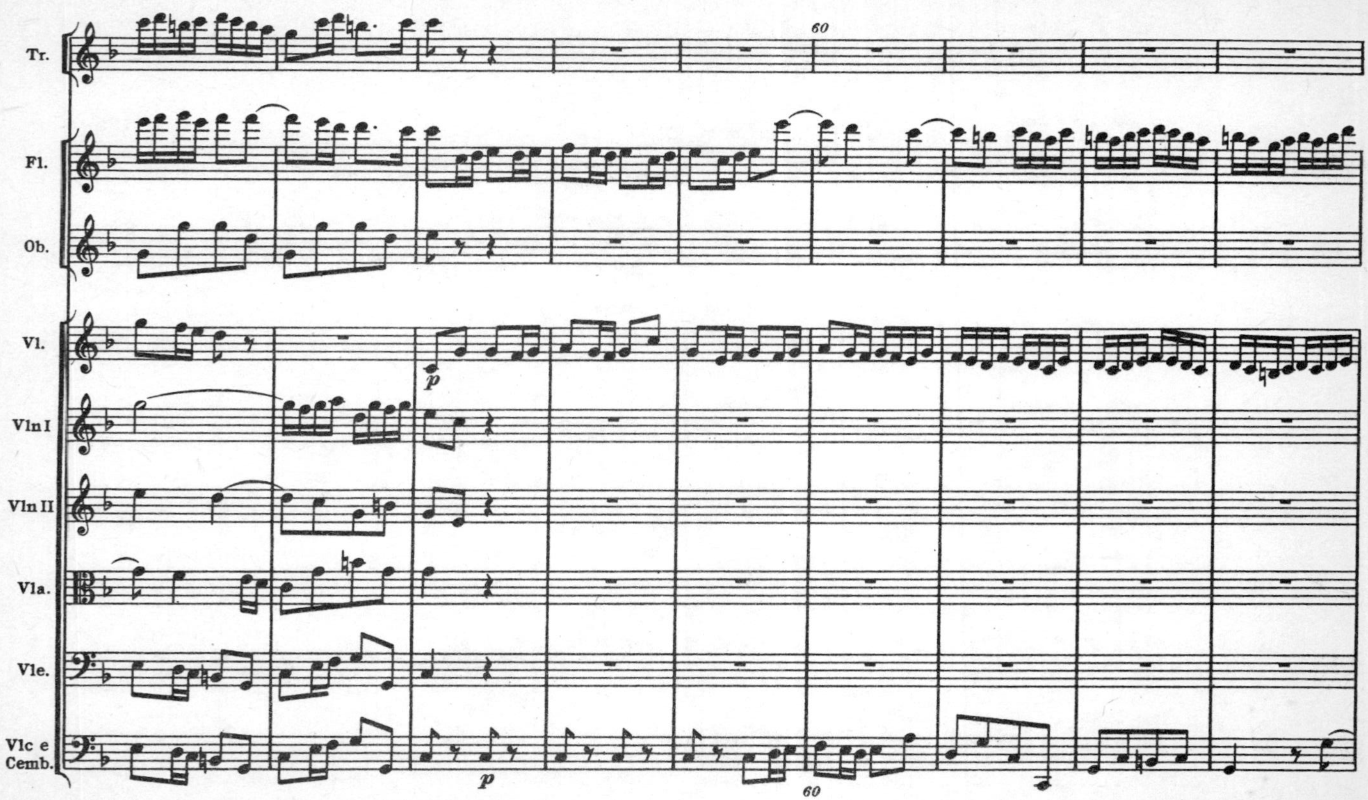
60
Tr.
Fl.
Ob.
Vl.
Vln I
Vln II
Vla.
Vle.
Vlc e
Cemb.
p
p
60

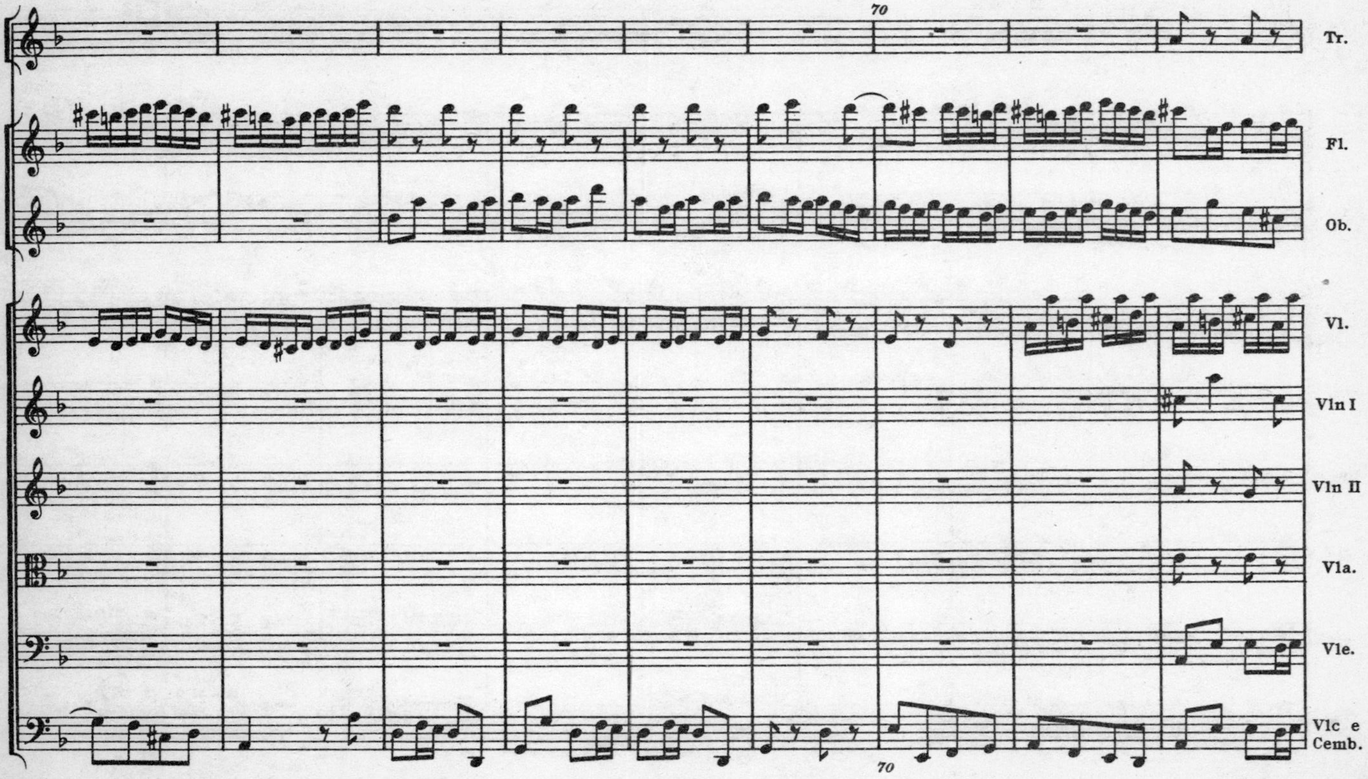
70
Tr.
Fl.
Ob.
Vl.
Vln I
Vln II
Vla.
Vle.
Vlc e
Cemb.
70

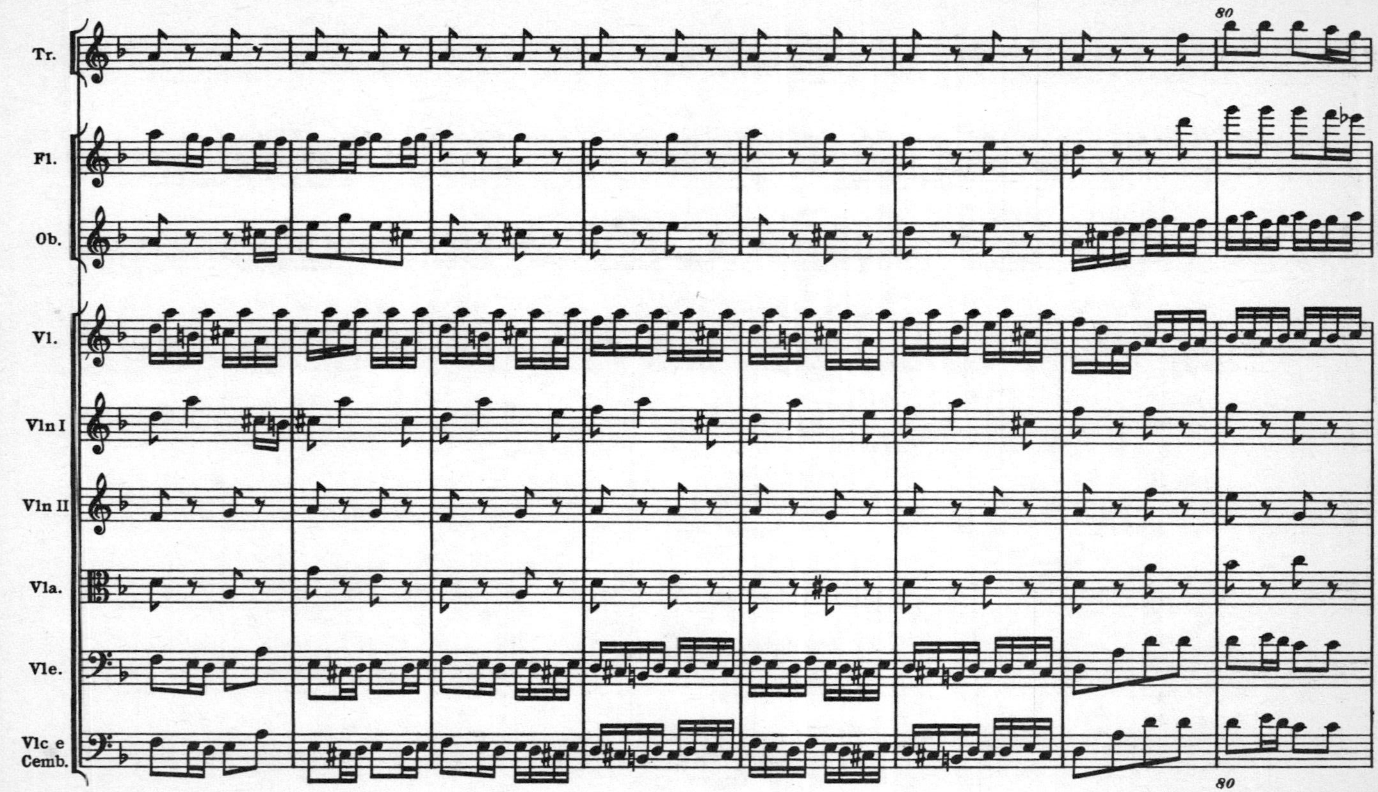

80
Tr.
Fl.
Ob.
Vl.
Vln I
Vln II
Vla.
Vle.
Vlc e Cemb.
80

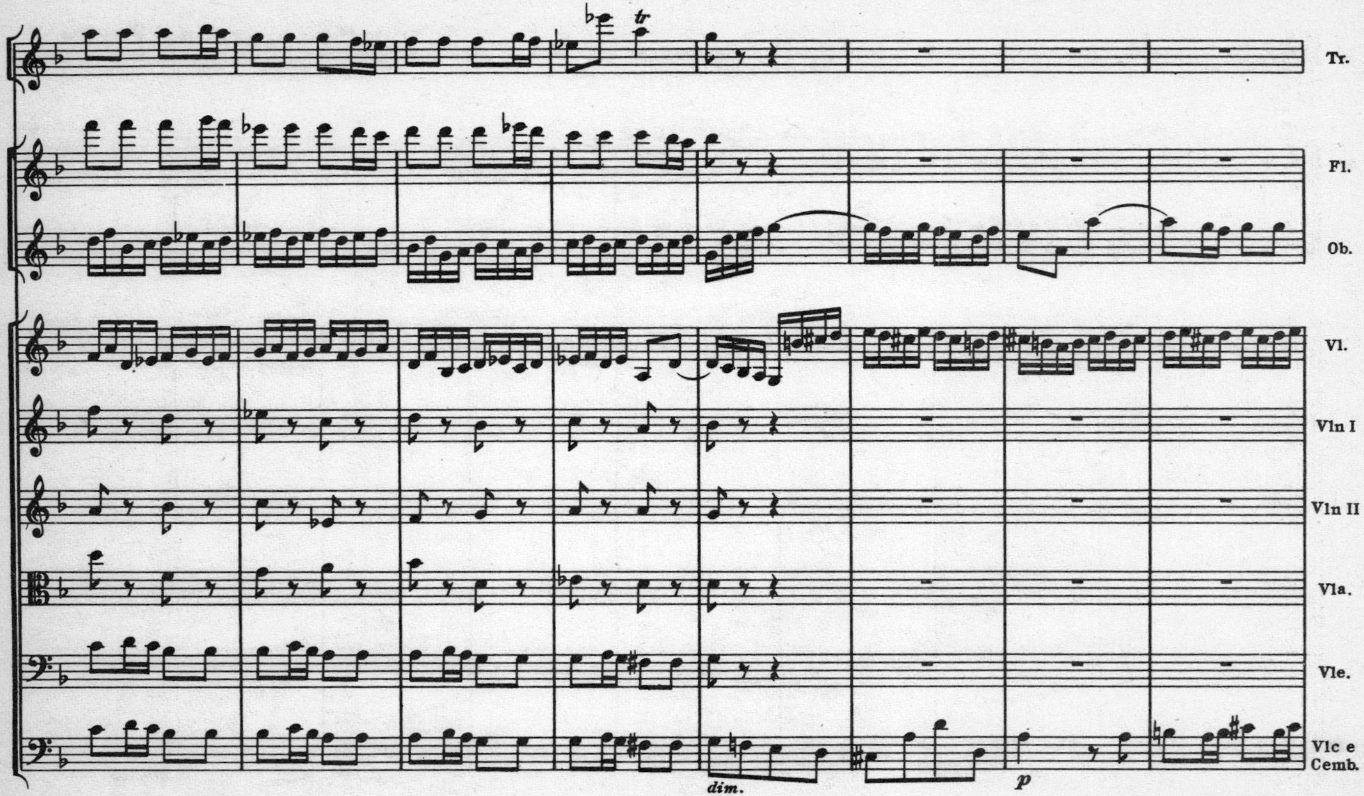
tr
Tr.
Fl.
Ob.
Vl.
Vln I
Vln II
Vla.
Vle.
Vlc e
Cemb.
dim.
p

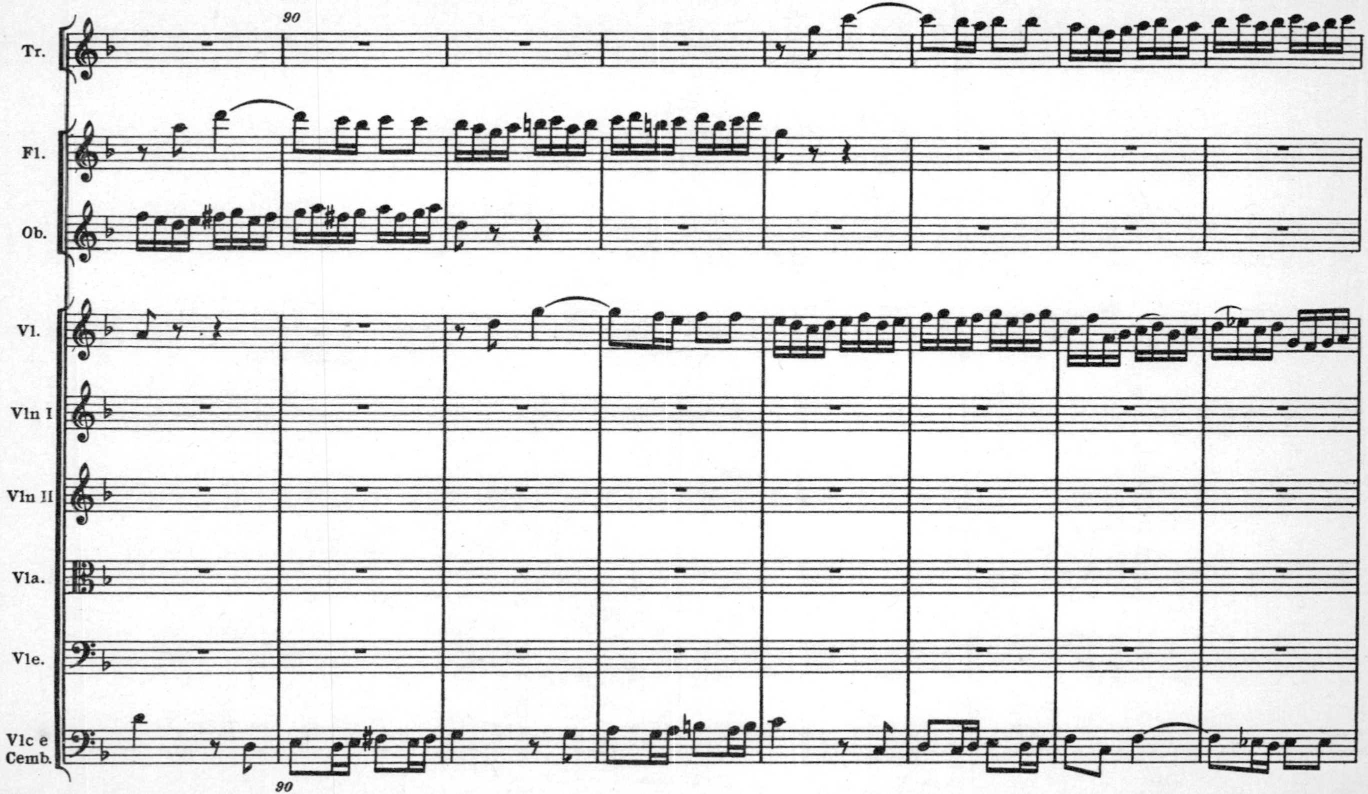
90
Tr.
Fl.
Ob.
Vl.
Vln I
Vln II
Vla.
Vle.
Vlc e Cemb.
90

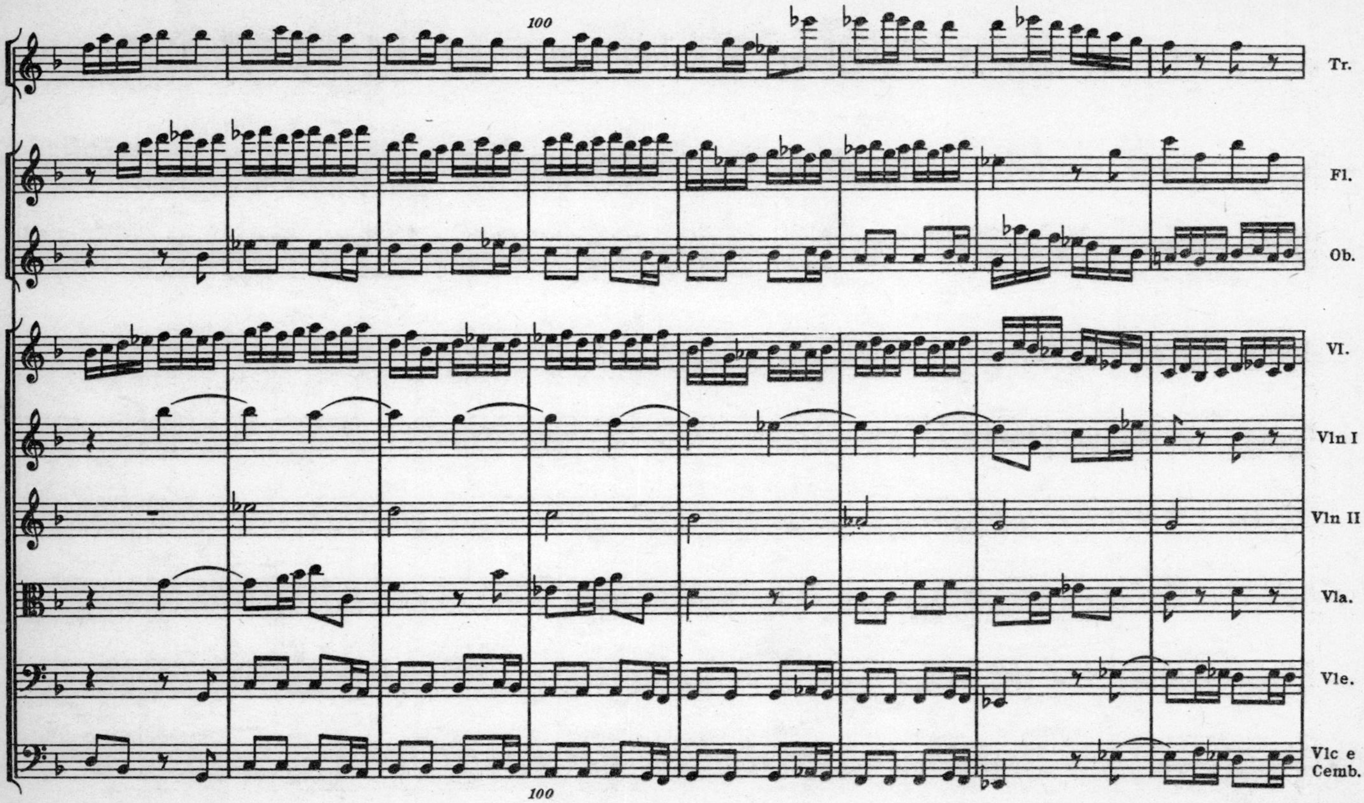
100
Tr.
Fl.
Ob.
Vl.
Vln I
Vln II
Vla.
Vle.
Vlc e
Cemb.
100

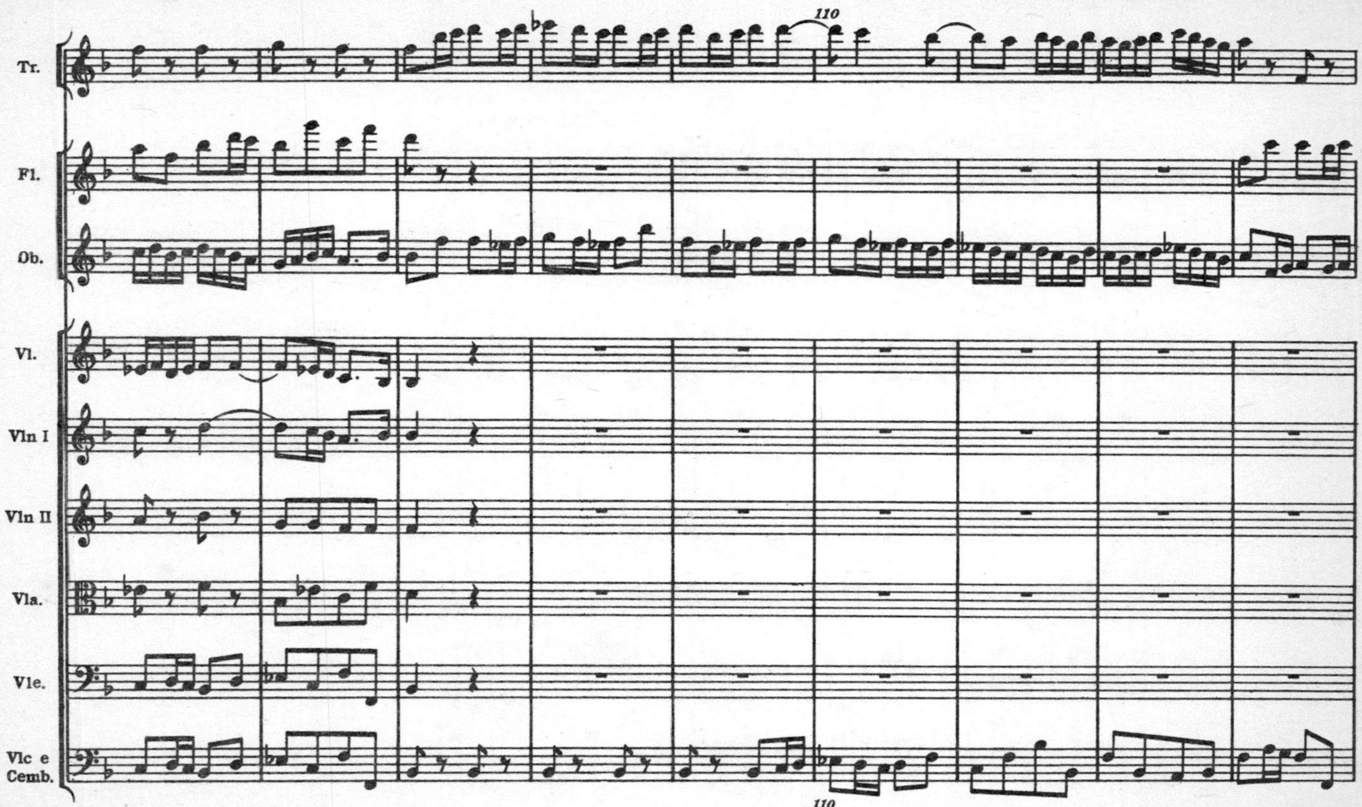
110
Tr.
Fl.
Ob.
Vl.
Vln I
Vln II
Vla.
Vle.
Vlc e
Cemb.
110

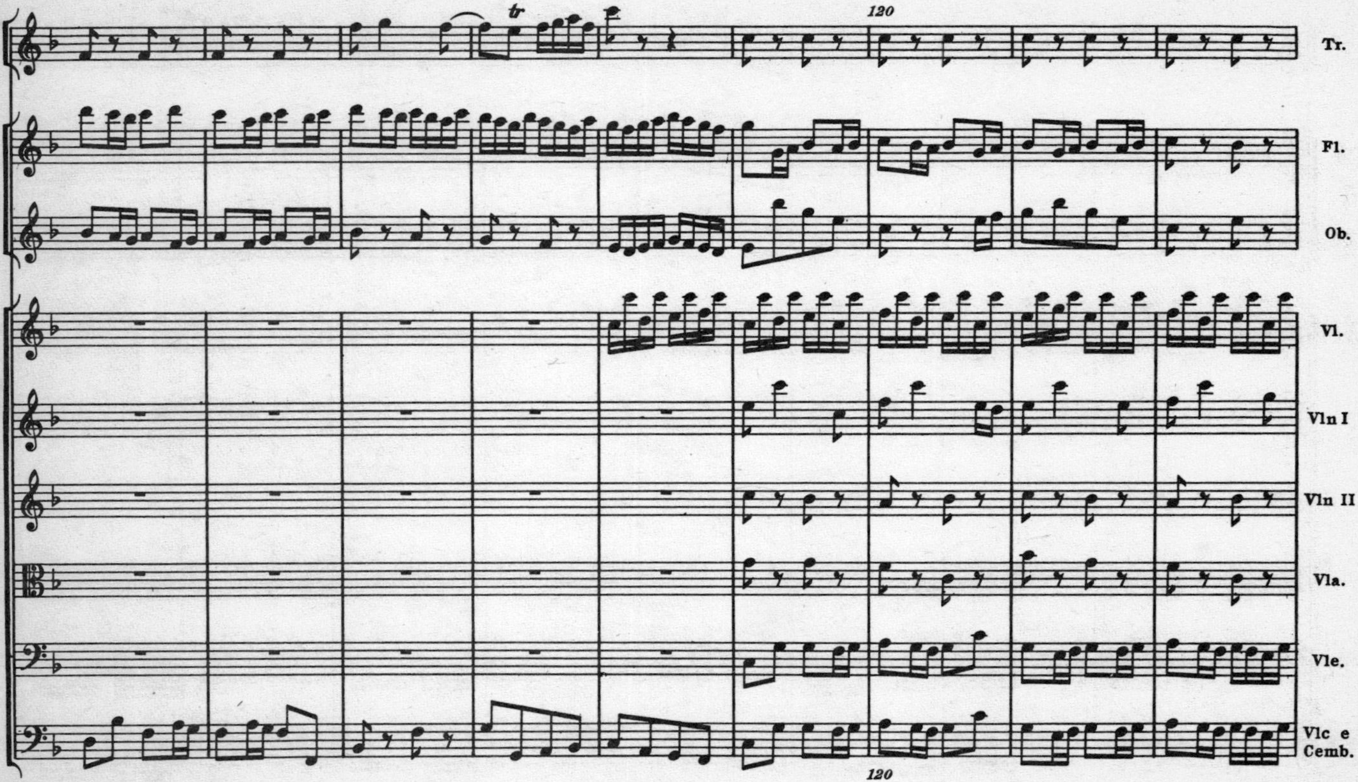
tr
120
Tr.
Fl.
Ob.
Vl.
Vln I
Vln II
Vla.
Vle.
Vlc e Cemb.
120

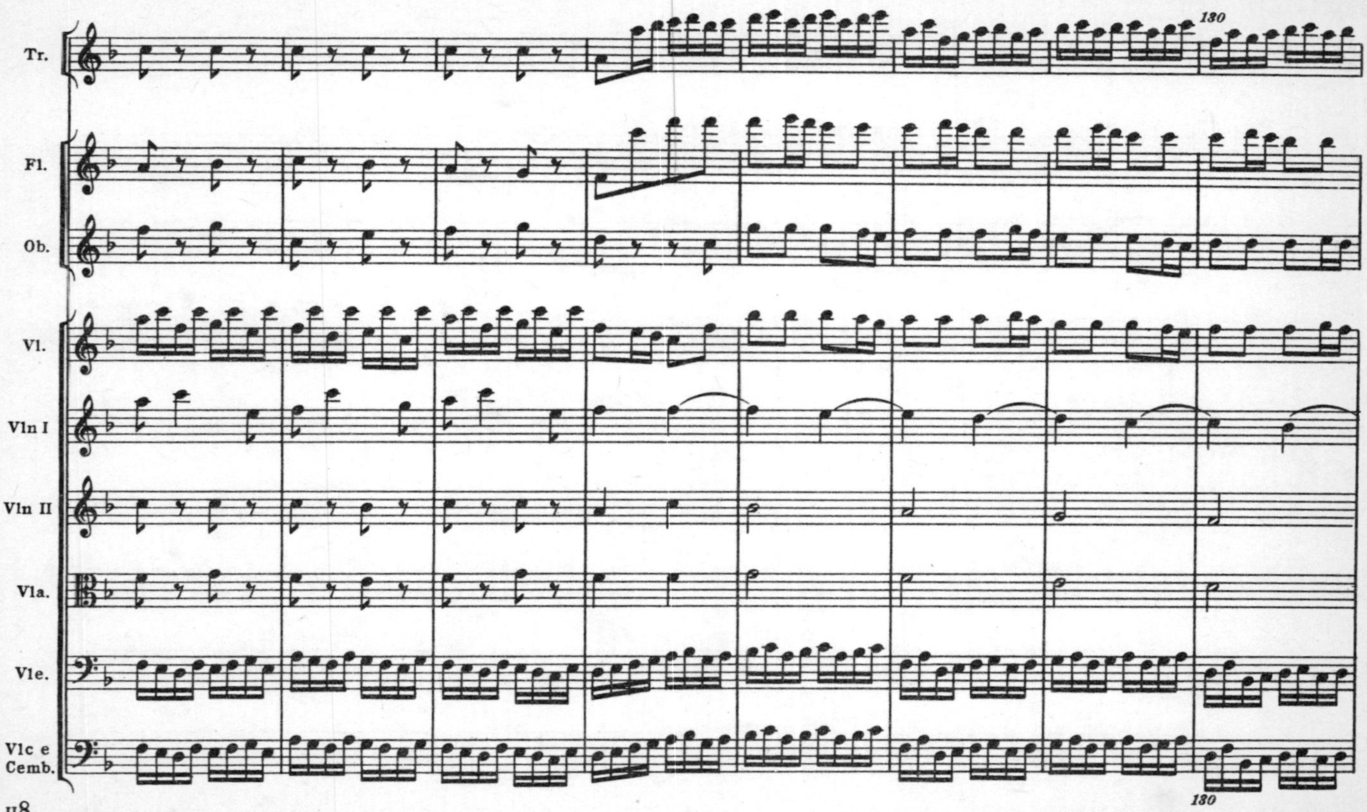
Tr.
Fl.
Ob.
Vl.
Vln I
Vln II
Vla.
Vle.
Vlc e
Cemb.
130
130

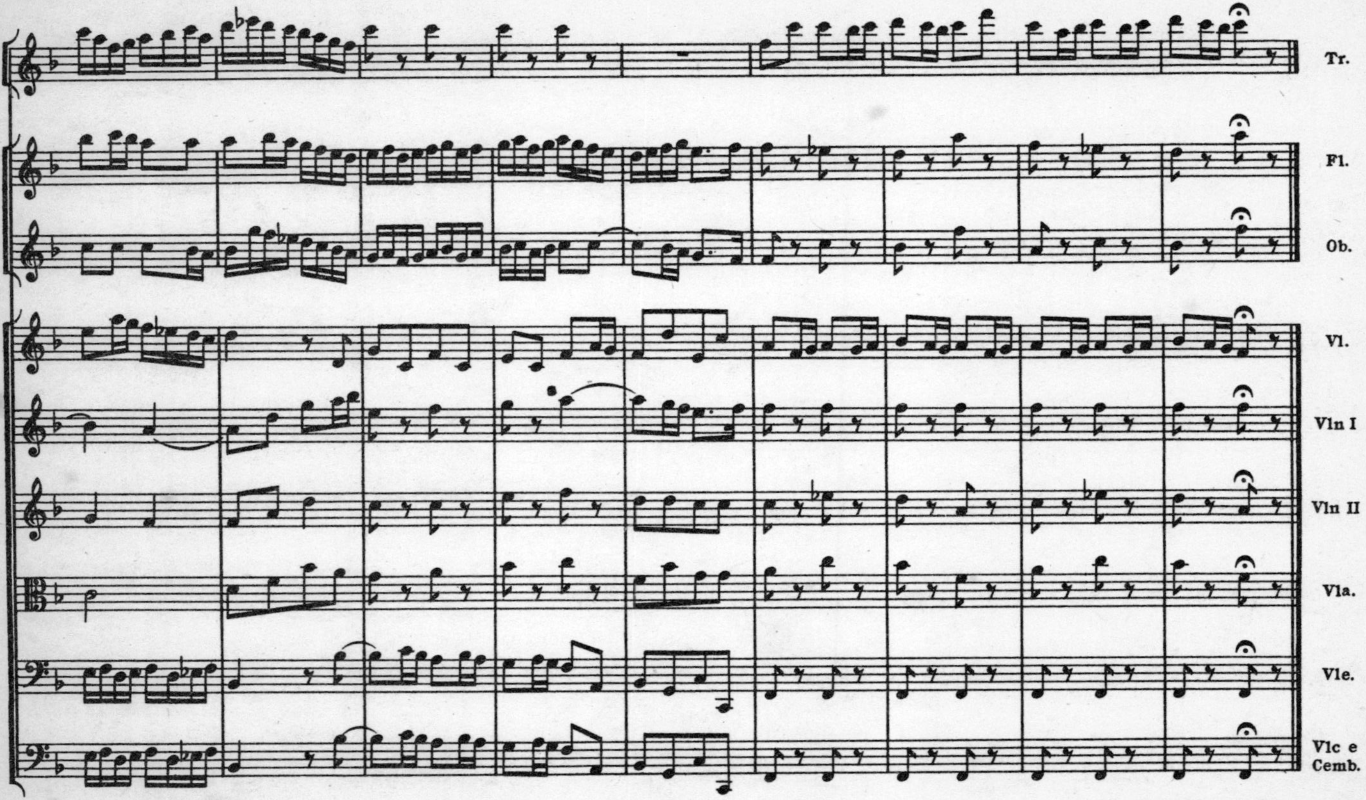
Tr.
Fl.
Ob.
Vl.
Vln I
Vln II
Vla.
Vle.
Vlc e Cemb.